MAKING
ALLOWANCES

© Chris Mansley 2003
Published by The Bluecoat Press, Liverpool
Book design by March Design, Liverpool
Printed by Ashford Colour Print, Gosport, Hants

ISBN 1 904438 09 1

ABOUT CHRIS MANSLEY

Chris Mansley has lived with severe Tourette Syndrome since early childhood. He is actively involved with the Tourette Syndrome (UK) Association, and is passionate in his desire to make the general public aware of the condition. He has had various articles published in newspapers and magazines, including the *British Medical Journal,* in which an edited version of his autobiographical account first appeared. He has also been interviewed on live world radio, and there can be no better advocate for his fellow sufferers.

Chris has worked tirelessly for eight long years to bring *Making Allowances* to publication, and those who read the seventeen very moving accounts, will be left in no doubt as to the true nature of this devastating condition.

MAKING ALLOWANCES

Personal accounts of
Tourette Syndrome

Compiled by Chris Mansley

The Bluecoat Press

CONTENTS

FOREWORD

Gilles de la Tourette Syndrome remains a somewhat neglected disorder, on the borderlands between neurology and psychiatry. Up until twenty-five years ago it was considered an exotic disorder rarely encountered by medical practitioners and frequently associated with psychotic illness. Fortunately, this misconception has now been corrected, and as a result of considerable media interest, Tourette Syndrome is now receiving a much higher public profile.

Despite this, and increased interest from medical practitioners, it remains an enigma. We know that Gilles de la Tourette Syndrome represents the severe end of the spectrum of tic disorders and that it is closely intertwined with obsessional-compulsive behavioural traits, but the biological explanations underlying its phenomenology remain obscure. Major research interest at present concentrates on the hunt for a gene, or several gene mutations, brain mapping in trying to identify the areas of the central nervous system which are dysfunctional, and the role of immunological factors in causation.

Chris Mansley's compilation of patients' and carers' moving accounts of what it is like to live with this quixotic and baffling condition, is to be welcomed. I wish this labour of love every success and hope that it will be widely read by both health professionals and the general public.

Professor Andrew Lees.
Medical advisor to the Tourette Syndrome (UK) Association.

PREFACE

'Nothing in life is to be feared. It is only to be understood.'
These words of Marie Curie, help illustrate how ignorance and misunderstanding can create fear towards Tourette Syndrome, probably one of the most complex disorders known to man. One purpose of this book is to help nurture an awareness and understanding of Tourette Syndrome and to dispel some of the myths and fears which surround the condition.

Tourette Syndrome is idiosyncratic, bizarre, irritating and draining, but ultimately it is about an imbalance in neurological functioning and a curtailment of the freedom which one would otherwise take for granted. Tourette Syndrome brings with it both destructive and constructive forces and such is its complexity, it has to be felt and experienced rather than merely described. Many who suffer from it often have their potential for success in life, or their relationships, destroyed before they can even get started, due to an overall shunning by society.

This book comprises seventeen very different, but varied accounts of people with TS from across the United Kingdom, both from the sufferer's and the parent's perspective. Each account dramatically outlines how the condition has transformed their whole lives. Some parts you may find sad, or even negative, while other parts are overwhelmingly emotional.

Within this book, a genuine attempt is made to communicate the real nature of TS and bring about a greater understanding of the way in which it impacts upon the lives of both sufferers and their families. Whoever reads it, and we hope there will be many, will gain greater understanding if they bear in mind that this condition is totally beyond control, that it comes with life itself, and that until there is a cure, it deserves as much investigation and support as possible. We feel very strongly that the time is right for this book, and since we have all suffered in silence for so long, we feel passionately that the true story of TS can only be told by those with personal experience.

It takes compassion, empathy and understanding to care for Tourettes sufferers, and as all we ask from society is for people to make an allowance for our behaviour, the only title for a book such as this can be: *Making Allowances*.

Chris Mansley

'LIFE' FOR TOURETTES

Chris Mansley

Born in a two up two down terrace in Preston, Lancashire, in 1962, even at a few months of age I exhibited hyperactive behaviour and incessant crying, to such an extent that a brain scan was undertaken which proved negative. Tourette Syndrome first physically manifested itself at the age of two, when I displayed tics such as eye blinking, shaking my head and shoulder shrugging. The acting out of compulsive destructions towards objects and people occurred at the age of three, and from then onwards, it just seemed as though my parents were constantly reprimanding me. I started school at four and, shortly after, commented to my parents that I didn't feel normal and that I wasn't like other kids at school. I told them that I thought something was wrong with me, but I remember them responding that a four-year-old child couldn't possibly know something was wrong with him and my problem was that I was just an attention-seeker. I felt rubbished by their attitude towards me.

Little did I know that I was about to spend the next twenty-seven years of my life desperately searching for what I knew deep down was some sort of neuro-biological disorder, and the rest of my life coping with the common associated phenomena which are an integral part of Tourettes.

At the age of eight I moved to the Blessed Sacrament junior school when my family moved to Ribbleton. Between the ages of seven and eight the compulsive behaviour increased in severity and a social worker was called in, due to concerns all round. She observed the compulsive behaviour which manifested itself in motor tics, compulsive grunting, sniffing, touching, counting, checking, twirling in circles, nipping and squeezing people, throwing things, occasional obscene gestures (Copopraxia), repetition of other people's words (Echolalia), repeating my own words (Palilalia), repeating other people's body movements (Echopraxia), and throat clearing.

All these symptoms waxed and waned and some would go into remission for a while, only to return again. Ten per cent of Tourettes sufferers compulsively swear (Coprolalia), but fortunately this did not manifest itself in me, but I would compulsively trip people up, sometimes not aware that I was doing it. I would nip, squeeze and tease my sisters, slam cups down to establish how hard I could do it before they would break, throw household articles around the room, even touch people's genitals and kick footballs through windows, but the irony of it all was that I really did not want to do it. I also had this compulsion where every time I walked to the end of the road and wanted to turn left, I had to turn 360 degree to my right, (and vice versa when turning right), before I could carry on with my journey.

To establish how aware I was of my tics, and in an arduous effort to try and get rid of them, particularly the head shaking ones, I used to balance a number of books on my head in the hope that sheer willpower alone would keep me from shaking them off and would somehow soften the compulsion to do it again. But the immense anxiety I felt only made it worse. Whenever I had the compulsion to squat to the floor, I used to disguise it by tripping up on myself first. Whenever I wanted to just touch the floor, I used to disguise it by pretending to drop my keys. Many Coprolalia sufferers often disguise their obscenities with a cough, and have even been known to shove things into their mouths so as not to be heard by anyone.

I have been told by my parents (although I can't remember doing this because I was obviously in a 'fog state' at the time), that when we had guests round for dinner, I used to walk into the room, stripping my clothes off and lassoing all the ornaments in sight, only to find myself coming round and not knowing what I'd spent the last fifteen minutes doing. On some days I would just sit there in a chair rocking backwards and forwards in sheer disturbance.

On reflection, I think I may also have had one of the autistic spectrum disorders, as I lived a large proportion of my childhood in a world of my own, often finding it very difficult to grasp any kind of reality to life. On occasions, I was sent home from school for having some kind of outburst, and upon being asked what had happened, I had no memory of it at all. In fact, I had no recollection of being at school at all on that day. I had no sense of time either. What I thought were minutes, were apparently hours that had gone by. My parents thought I was being rude when I would leave a friend standing at the front door for half an hour, whilst wandering obliviously around the house. I thought I'd only been gone minutes. It sounds funny, but at mealtimes I would be given a lovely meal to eat, but didn't enjoy it because I couldn't remember what it tasted like. I simply couldn't remember eating it. Only by sheer effort and determination over years of personal growth, I am now compos mentis enough to write a story such as this.

I had, and still have, an obsession with numbers, whereby even numbers feel good and odd numbers feel bad. When I touch things compulsively, stir a cup of coffee, brush my teeth, or even let the phone ring, it has to fall on an even number; otherwise I am convinced something bad might happen. The way I touch things has to be done in a symmetrical pattern so that it feels 'just right' to me, and if I feel it hasn't been touched right, I have to start all over again until it's completed just right. The most serious compulsion I have is of touching things I know are dangerous, like hot cooker rings, and one of the most embarrassing makes me look inept; I ask someone a simple question to which I already know the answer. My obsessive thoughts wouldn't allow a song or tune that I had been listening to on the radio to peter out. I would walk into rooms opening and closing the door for a certain number of times, until it felt just right, and would then proceed to turn the light switch on and off repeatedly until that also felt just right. Anyone outside would have thought there was a disco going on! As a painfully shy young man, I understood the urgency of disguising such embarrassing behaviour, but suffered immense anxiety if the routines were not carried out properly.

I will never forget the time when my eldest sister threw a sod of soil through a neighbour's window, and then blamed it on me, saying it was one of my compulsions. There was probably an element of jealousy, as I was shown more attention than her due to my obvious learning difficulties. However, I went without pocket money for weeks to pay for a new window.

People will often ask me what it feels like to have a tic. This is a difficult question to answer. As a child with a limited vocabulary, I could only describe it as an overwhelming urge to twitch. However, this word carries emotional overtones with me as an adult, so I now prefer to use the correct term, 'tic'. 'Premonitory urges' is a term used to describe what it feels like when you feel a tic coming on. Some sufferers describe this as a mental urge, some as a physical one. A need to tic is an intense feeling which, if left unsatisfied, makes you feel as though you are going to burst. Unless I can physically tic, all of my mental thoughts and energies unavoidably centre on ticcing, until I am able to let them out. A tic is like having an itch that you just have to scratch, but the frustration you feel is like having that itch in the middle of your back where you can't reach it.

As an example, I will ask people to try and stop blinking, or hold their breath for five minutes, to see how they would feel. The anxiety would probably drive them mad. Having TS means that anxiety builds up in your body, and you just have to tic it away. Completing the tic relieves the anxiety, but it is soon brought back when you feel the next compulsion to tic again. People accuse you of having no willpower, but all the willpower in the world wouldn't stop me from ticcing, because the cause is neurological. Tics and compulsions can be suppressed to a degree, but always with the sacrifice of even greater anxiety.

You could view it as though 'normal' people are on automatic pilot. Every day they act naturally without thinking about their movements, whereas the more severe Tourettes sufferer, with motor tics, has to think about every movement, as though on manual pilot.

Understanding tics is one thing, but coming to grips with obsessions and compulsions can be a little more taxing. It seems that there is a significant curtailment of inhibition within the Tourette brain, that would normally be filtered out in any healthy one. In Tourettes, the things that we know are socially unacceptable seem to fuel the compulsion. An example of this is when I attended the 1998 US International Conference on TS, during which one evening was allocated for a sightseeing Potomac cruise, and a large coach took members with Tourettes to the boat. In transit, one member had the compulsion to repeatedly bash the window with his arm. The coach driver pulled over and asked him politely to stop bashing the window, as they were quite fragile, being designed to fall out in an emergency. What happened next was typical of the inhibition factor in Tourettes. A large number of fellow sufferers on the coach started doing the same thing.

Before receiving any kind of medication, the most complex type of tic that I experienced was my compulsion to execute a specific number of tics before picking up a glass of water, for example, but not being able to tic until I had thumped myself quite violently. It was as if by hitting myself, it sort of released a pressure safety valve in me (like unlocking a door), enabling me to finish my task. This would often result in me going catatonic. In public, I was so ashamed and embarrassed by my condition, that I would walk into lamp-posts; I didn't have the confidence to hold my head up and cope with seeing people gaping at me, and therefore watch where I was going.

Some nights I would cry myself to sleep, praying for something to rid me of what I thought were demons, asking for this so-called Jesus to come into my life, only to be left feeling that no one was listening, no one was answering. Born-again Christians now tell me that I didn't pray hard enough. I felt that if this chap loved me so much, he would be guiding me in the right direction; helping me find a diagnosis and a safe environment in which I could obtain help and support. I began to feel that if heaven was a place on earth, it was a hell of a place to find.

I hated God and hated myself for how he had created me; especially since none of my family had been burdened with this awesome condition. I strongly suspect my father to be the carrier of the TS genes, but he was totally in remission from having the tics, instead, just having the associated disorders of Obsessive Compulsive Disorder (OCD) and Attention Deficit Hyperactivity Disorder (ADHD).

My parents were probably the most incompatible of couples you could ever imagine. They used to argue for as many hours as humanly possible throughout most days of each week, in front of us children. This used to disturb me immensely and was even making me contemplate at the age of five, whether or not I should ever get married myself. My father used to try to involve us children in those arguments. When I didn't agree with what he had said, or done, his rage used to be turned on me.

My mother, a nurse, used to imitate my symptoms and said that they frustrated her intensely. She would shout for my sisters to come for lunch and then add, "… and where's that bloody lad?" I used to often think that they were not my real parents and did not love their children equally. I was regarded as the black sheep of the family and held in low esteem as a frequent pest, when compared to my infallible, angelic sisters. I feel like they will hate me for eternity.

When a Tourettes child reaches out for emotional warmth to his family, it is often carried out in a compulsive way, for example with a nip or a nudge. When I reached to my family for warmth in that way, it was sometimes requited to me with a raising of the arm from my parents. It happened often enough, from an early age, that I started to relate to pain as warmth – a feeling which permeated into adulthood for a while. Whenever I was shown any physical affection from anyone, maybe a cuddle or even just holding or shaking hands with a partner, I felt like apologising. The emotional pain and embarrassment I felt was in a league of its own.

Human contact is something you long for, but instead of being able to reciprocate, along comes the Tourettes compulsion to nip and squeeze. I felt, and still do feel such remorse, guilt and shame for all that I did, despite friends telling me that I wasn't to blame. The words, "naughty, bad, disobedient, little boy" still haunt me today, as I feel that there wasn't a day went by without my mother repeatedly echoing this phrase down my ear. My greatest wish, to prove to my family that I wasn't the naughty bad child they thought I was, was to be put on standby for another twenty years until a diagnosis of neurological origin was revealed. If only I could have proved to them at the time, that inexplicable forces inside my body were controlling me, a lot of trauma could have been spared.

I was referred to a child psychiatrist who diagnosed me as having Schizophrenia. It was at this stage that I experienced familiar places looking strange to me, and insisted that I had never been there before – the fog state. I confessed all my symptoms and compulsions to my priest as I thought I was possessed by the devil. He agreed with me, and I was asked to say many Hail Marys and Our Fathers for the forgiveness of my sins.

In 1971, at the age of nine, I was persuaded by my parents, although to me it felt like bribery and coercion, to move into a children's home run by Lancashire County Council for children with severe behavioural problems. What with my father having an alcohol problem, and on occasion being violent, and me suffering from a mystery illness, it was too much for the rest of the family to handle. Social Services suggested that one of us had to go. Since my father was the breadwinner, and Social Services didn't offer support for single parents in the UK back in the 1960s, instead of divorcing her wicked husband, she took the easier option of getting rid of me. In January 1972 I reluctantly allowed them to give me away. With hindsight, I now realise that I lost a family that I never really had, as they didn't really know me, and have never properly, in my opinion, taken the time to try to do so.

This home was very strictly run, which, given my compulsions, made life very difficult for me. However, I did learn how to partially suppress my symptoms, which only served to increase my levels of anxiety. For the following six months I studied in a special educational unit within the grounds of the home for children with severe learning disabilities, and started learning the beginnings of how to read and write. Certain members of staff at the home used what was known as the 'pin down' technique. For being naughty, or in my case compulsive, I would be made to stand on one of the coloured tiles on the floor, in the dark, for hours, sometimes with other children, before being allowed to go to bed in the early hours of the morning, missing both my tea and supper. When I reported them to my parents, the staff accused me of lying and pinned me down again for telling my parents.

Within the first week I was there, I was in trouble. We had to go to bed very early at this home and, as we couldn't sleep at such an early hour, we naturally started talking. Apparently the staff heard us. The following evening, as we were all going to bed, the six of us were all lined up against the landing banister rail and birched, one after the other. All the other children were made to watch as a deterrent. Perhaps this was regarded as excessive, because the following week a new member of staff appeared at the home as a replacement.

I was given the option of returning home if I didn't like it after a one-week trial period. However, after expressing my concerns to my parents of both physical and mental abuse, I was accused of fabricating the seven-day trial period and left to stew there for the next seven years of my childhood, with only fortnightly visits home for the weekend, and without any further visits to me from my family over that period. I complained saying, "I have my rights," to which I was told, "Young man, you have no rights, you are just a child." I was absolutely devastated at this news and in not knowing why this decision had been made, I sank into a deep depression. It wasn't long before I started to feel like a forgotten child, lost in the system. I felt betrayed by my own family, and not knowing how long I was going to be there for, I started to feel very guilty – I must have been horrendously behaved back at home to be given this long sentence. On those fortnightly visits home, I used to ask my parents how long I would have to live there for. Their stock answer was, "Until you can behave in a civilised manner," which compounded those feelings of endless guilt. Subconsciously, I think I have carried that guilt with me through to my adulthood, as I am consciously aware of seeking approval in my adult relationships.

One of the female staff there had an obsession with the toilets. If a pupil wanted to go to the toilet, he or she would have to ask her permission to use it. After you had been, she conducted a personal inspection. If you had had "no results" (as she fondly termed it), you were reprimanded, and retired to your bed for the rest of the day for wasting her time. I'll never forget the time when I was fourteen and a staff member dragged me out on to the landing by my hair at 2am and tried to strangle me as I grappled with the iron banister rails because, he claimed, he had heard rumours that I had been smoking. As it happens, I had, but I didn't think that justified the punishment. Numerous children ran away while I lived there, only to be escorted back by the police. I still have regular nightmares of that place today, twenty-five years on.

After finishing at the special educational unit, later on that year I started to study at St Bernard's junior school where I had, by that time, developed a 'Hitler' walk compulsion. Crowds of children would line up behind me in single file to copy the walk, only to have some teachers look down on us from the staff room in fits of laughter – whilst no attempt was ever made to stop it. Nor did they take proper steps when a few children tried setting fire to my school clothes as I had told them, at that stage, that I thought I was possessed by the devil.

At this stage, I had developed compulsive spitting (another symptom of TS) and was given a mop and bucket to keep next to me in the classroom to clean up after myself. I remained there for two years, achieving moderate progress, then moved to the high school next door in 1974. There, I learned to play the guitar, which I discovered gave me temporary relief from my symptoms whilst I concentrated on playing. I also excelled athletically – throwing the javelin, eventually for Preston Athletic Club. Nevertheless, the next five years saw me being bullied by a few individuals but protected by a very good friend of mine, Stuart McDonald – my knight in shining armour. It was only in my final year, after suffering a constant battering ram of ridicule from one individual, that I completely lost all control. I went hysterical whilst in a fight – placing him in hospital for medical treatment. He never bothered me after that, showing me the utmost respect!

Generally, though, throughout my years in senior school, I can't begin to fully explain how intensely isolated I felt being on the receiving end of that constant derision. I heard the sniggers, the giggles, the derogatory names (Noddy, Blinky, Zombie and Lurch to name but a few), the whispers, and then the empty seats beside me. Following a tic, I would hear the children behind me say, "He did, he did. Just watch him and see". I became conscious of every voluntary movement I made, only to fear the repercussions that inevitably followed the next involuntary tic or compulsion – yet another bundle of laughs. A type of laughter that is directed right at you, and not with you. You could tell they were really enjoying it as well. The sheer power of those laughs moulded me into the empty, inferior child I had become.

Some teachers found my condition difficult to cope with and one in particular would imitate and ridicule the tics and compulsive behaviour. I used to have one compulsion to repeatedly open and close my mouth. The teacher in question used to throw wooden board dusters at me telling me to, "Stop catching flies". In metalwork, the teacher used to have a habit of bashing the handle five times after forging the metal from the fire-furnace, (thinking about it now, he might have suffered from OCD), and I used to have the compulsion to copy him in exactly the same way (Echopraxia). However, as he thought I must have been winding him up, I got six of the leather strap in the annexe. What didn't help matters at all was that I then had the compulsion to move my hands away every time he swung the strap down, hence another six of the strap, repeated until my hands bled.

My concentration span, due to Attention Deficit Disorder (ADD), at times was very poor. For example, the teacher might say to the class, "Now children, turn to page fifty-two please," and I would miss what she had said. I could read a book to the class quite fluently, page after page after page, yet not take any of it in at all. This may sound silly, but at the time, I didn't know that what I was reading was a story, or that there was anything to take in! Yet I know I'm not Dyslexic. I would understand the answer to a complex mathematical equation one day, and not know how I had worked it out the next.

If you tell a person they are thick and stupid for long enough, like I was told, they will start to act and become that person – a self-fulfilling prophecy. The impatience of some of my peers is probably where a lot of my insecurities came from. Not a day went by when I did not receive ridicule or humiliation from both teachers and children. This was particularly hurtful when arising from attractive teenage girls whom I was fond of. Despite my learning difficulties, and much to my own amazement, I managed to acquire eight CSE passes on finishing school.

In 1979, at sixteen years of age, I left school, and although it was such a relief to finish my seven-year sentence at the children's home, returning home meant confronting the disgust of my father, who greeted my renewed presence with threats rather than offering me a warm welcome. It seemed that I just got in the way, and he frequently hinted that I should be looking for a home of my own, until I left home a few years later.

Upon starting employment, I worked initially in a pet shop, then cleaning cars and eventually as an assistant in a butcher's shop. I started to want something more secure, so I then made 180 job inquiries, eventually leading to three interviews. One of those companies wanted me back for another interview, and then another, only to be told I wasn't suitable for the position.

I eventually found employment two months later via my uncle, who, at the time, was a Clerk of Works officer for the local council, as a fitter's mate working in the central heating trade. I was despised, initially, by a few colleagues, for obtaining the job via someone from the inside, but this wore off in time. For the following two years, however, some of the qualified fitters made my life a misery. They quickly gave me the nickname I once thought was well behind me in life – Noddy – because I was always shaking my head. On one unforgettable occasion, a refill of coal was ordered for a deep coalbunker at a school which I was working at. The filling began, despite me being down there clearing it out at the time. I was too frightened to complain, as I was not in any trades union that could have supported me, and I was told by other colleagues to keep my mouth shut, as I was lucky to be in work.

After working there for a short while, an employee told me that, as I was only a fitter's mate, I wouldn't be qualified as a professional central heating engineer at the end of my training. I suggested they indenture me at college in order to learn the theory, but they refused, and added that if I started a course during working hours, they would terminate my employment. As an alternative, and to become qualified in at least something, I started an evening class at Blackburn Polytechnic and studied to become a welder.

At that time in my life, I was able to suppress the tics long enough to keep a welding rod still to complete a beaded run. However, back at work, the intimidation continued. The engineers (unaware of my new-found knowledge of indentureship) pointed out to me that "treating apprentices like shit" was nothing new, and that when I had qualified as a fitter, I would then be in a position to treat my apprentices like shit too. So when they made me redundant two years later, it really was a blessing in disguise. I never did complete my training in the central heating trade.

A year later, I walked away from the polytechnic with a City & Guilds qualification as a welder under my belt. As I got older, however, my symptoms appeared to get worse. I am not sure whether the Tourettes got worse (as many specialists say it often gets better with age) or my ability to suppress the symptoms was reduced. Either way, I can no longer practise my trade, as I cannot keep the welding rod still long enough.

It was whilst I was still eighteen, that I met my first love, Julie. After admiring her for months, I finally decided to pluck up the courage to phone her, even though I was a perfect stranger (being the friend of a friend's sister). Not thinking she would want anything to do with me, due to my lack of self-worth, I was shocked and pleasantly surprised that she agreed to a date with me. Julie was just seventeen years old, and training to work with the elderly; a career she had chosen from an early age and seemed to be committed to.

From day one, my feelings for her were very strong, and for the first time in my life, I felt that I belonged to someone. She, in return, seemed to have real feelings for me; or so I thought. It soon became apparent that Julie had an ex-boyfriend who was from Kuwait and had been studying in Britain, but had gone back home to live, and, guess what? She was missing him terribly. I was selfishly hoping he wouldn't come back to Britain, and that, in time, her feelings for me would grow stronger. Unfortunately for me, they didn't.

Months were passing by and I was falling deeply in love with Julie. The stress of trying my level best to suppress my TS symptoms, in case of rejection, was taking its toll on me. The love I was showing her was becoming increasingly unrequited, and I could see that it was only a matter of time before the relationship fizzled out.

I'm not sure whether she got fed up with me, or was missing her ex, or maybe both, but, whatever, our relationship came to an end. I still see her from time to time. She is married now with three children, and although it took me a good ten years to get over her, to this day I don't think she will ever realise just how much I loved her. She meant the world to me, and I've yet to meet someone who could sweep me off my feet like she did.

My life's tumbles seemed to be reaping vengeance on me at this time in my life and as I seemed to slip into another depression, I developed an inferiority complex, which was to be one of my worst problems to overcome. A fear of people in general brought about panic attacks, whether I was mixing in social places, or even walking into a shop and asking for a loaf of bread. I was referred to a psychologist, which led to me being treated with hypnotherapy. Unfortunately, this was not successful, as he said I wasn't the suggestible type. Although a very competent psychologist, he wasn't to get to the root of the problem, as he didn't specialise in the field of psychotherapy, which might have proved more positive for the secondary psychological factors which have now been established as being associated with TS. In fact, this inferiority complex took hold of me to such a degree that, one particular week when I travelled to see him, I walked the ten miles home because I couldn't bring myself to go into a garage and face the cashier to pay for my petrol after my motorbike ran out of fuel.

Shortly after being on the dole again, I acquired a few temporary factory jobs, and although it was unusual to be under the same roof all day, I faced very little derision. I then worked on and off for the next four years, registering with a casual company called Manpower which originated in the United States. Manpower sub-contracted me out to other companies for semi-skilled work on a temporary basis, without being strictly vetted by each individual firm that hired me. This was a godsend when you take into consideration that it can be very difficult to obtain employment when you have an affliction like TS. I acquired no less than 200 different jobs with this agency over the following four years, taking the rough with the smooth. It necessitated me being available to work with anybody, at any time, any place, anywhere, and having to travel long distances working away, sometimes staying in hotels.

By this time in my life, I really wanted to start travelling and seeing the world. So, as Tourettes waxes and wanes, and as I was only a casual worker required to work intermittently, when I was experiencing healthier periods, my itchy feet used to take me off abroad to work in other countries. My first employment abroad was working in the vineyards around Europe where the pay was quite good, but you had to work very hard. I even spent some time on a French fairground making candy floss, getting my accommodation with a local religious movement in the French Alps.

Other years I would work in restaurants around the Mediterranean, and busking on the Greek islands with some Canadian friends I had met. There was only ever one individual in one of the vineyards that took umbrage to my Tourettes! I roughed it from time to time, although I will never regret my tours. I would often go back to be with my then French girlfriend who I'd met in one of the vineyards. This may sound strange, but on my tours, there was a nice feeling of experiencing total freedom by being anonymous in society. You're on nobody's books, nobody's computer database, nobody's council register waiting for some huge poll tax bill to come through the post, and every day is a new day, in a new town, meeting new people. Travelling while I was younger were the happiest days of my life. Though I would always come home to England when my Tourettes took a turn for the worse.

After returning to Britain in 1984, and spending the Christmas period working as a postman in my home town, I went back to working for Manpower again. At this point in time, my condition started to deteriorate, resulting in contractors phoning Manpower complaining of my suspected state of drug intoxication. The anxiety and stress I suffered because of the worsening of my Tourettes led me to experience feelings which were ultimately ascribed to neuro-biological causal factors, rather than alcohol, or drug-related ones. However, as a result of the complaints, my employment was terminated and I once again went back on the dole.

As time went by, my childhood memories were beginning to haunt me and I sank into despair. These feelings were compounded by the rejection I had felt from my parents and the children's home as a child. I was beginning to drift and was finding it increasingly difficult to keep my train of thought and cope with day-to-day living. I could feel myself sinking and withdrawing, knowing, subconsciously, that I was heading for a mental breakdown. I thought, if I can just develop new coping strategies, I can fight it off, but as I was running out of new ideas, I was drawn into a downward spiral.

My parents had asked me to find my own accommodation, and as I looked for a place of my own I soon began to realise that gaining employment is not the only thing you have difficulty in attaining when you suffer from Tourette Syndrome. My parents had suggested that I move into a flat that was in a run-down area, and didn't seem too bothered where I lived. I objected to this, as I wanted to live in healthier surroundings. Within forty-eight hours of looking for accommodation elsewhere, without my knowledge, my own mother forced me to leave my family home by means of a court order. I was refused a loan from her to set up on my own, and, as I had no money, I was left no option but to attend a local jumble sale to obtain basic household items to eat from.

Luckily, through a friend, I found a house to rent in a sought-after area in Preston. However, because of the dilapidated state it was in, I managed to talk the landlord into a two figure sum of only fifteen pounds a week. The house had been severely run down with ants and lice covering the window-sills and food and beer cans littering the floor. The vacuum cleaner had not seen daylight in a month of Sundays. I lived with another young man diagnosed as having acute Schizophrenia. As neither I nor he ever really saw eye to eye, he suddenly did a moonlight flit leaving a note complaining that I was too clean and tidy to live with.

By now, living on my own, I gradually detached myself from society, excluded, in effect, by virtue of the severity of my symptoms, which included bending down in the street to chin my knees, head-butting lamp-posts, licking walls, etc. Such symptoms are not the sort of things you would normally associate with a medical condition, and they elicited ridicule and derision wherever I went. One wonders at the mysteriousness of being drawn towards such unnatural forces, yet this is how the condition can be misconstrued as bad behaviour. I would have abdominal tics (tensing my stomach) until eventually I was sick due to the pain and nausea. In the line of my vision, I would compulsively run my hand around the outline of a building across the road, only to have people waving back at me as they thought I was waving at them.

Sounds like something out of Monty Python doesn't it? In the past I've unintentionally bought numerous cars and household appliances at auctions through having these compulsions. As you would imagine, it is imperative to warn auctioneers of this condition before buying up the entire auction stock. Indeed, sometimes you have to laugh, otherwise you cry.

The following experience of drawing money out from my local cashpoint machine is a case in point. When I first approached the machine there was nobody there. Moments later, an ambulance passed me in the street nearby. An overwhelming desire came over me to copy the wooing sound it was making at the top of my voice (Echophenomena), only to turn round and find a man standing behind me in the queue with the most bewildered look on his face!

The Job Centre continued to harass me with regard to undertaking work, which only served to increase my anxiety and stress levels. I tried very hard to fight and suppress my symptoms, but the stress and anxiety attached to my efforts produced headaches, black-outs and dizziness, all of which created dangerous situations, particularly when crossing roads, and cooking with boiling hot water. I became totally isolated from society for three and a half years, developing severe Agoraphobia and living the life of a recluse. Throughout this period, I had only three visits from my mother to deliver Christmas cards, and by this time, she was also offering me money. I remember throwing it back at her, saying, "You cannot buy me." I became really hard on myself, not allowing myself any pleasures in life. Then I realised – it was once other people that were abusing me – but now I was abusing myself. They say it's good to have friends, especially when you have no family to support you, but by this time all my so-called friends had deserted me, just when I needed them most. Now, being Agoraphobic, I was terrified of stepping out of the front door, even to go to the grocer's. Even the grass in my gardens grew out of control, as I feared the outdoors too much to tidy it up.

The 'pits' came when two hoax double-glazing representatives came to my house and mocked me on my own front door step. I wouldn't have thought anyone could stoop so low in life. I had become a prisoner of my illness, inside a body that had betrayed me, that tortured me throughout every waking hour of every day.

During this time I claimed sickness benefit, which lasted six months, after which I was reassessed by a DSS doctor who recognised that something was seriously wrong and suggested a GP referral to a specialist. I then went in receipt of Invalidity Benefit and joined many lengthy waiting lists for consultations with various doctors all over Britain – which all proved negative.

One psychiatrist, after telling him my symptoms, said I would be cured if I were to stop drinking coffee and go swimming! At one point the tics were so bad that I fractured my arm, and have now permanently damaged tendons and nerves in my back. It was disturbing looking at myself in the mirror whilst ticcing – it was as if I were having a seizure. It's strange, but unless you see your own reflection, you have no concept of exactly how you look to other people. It was hard to believe that the reflection was really me. Treatment consisted of sedation with high doses of Largactil, in order to exhaust the tics, and allow the bone to heal, as suitable medication was unknown to the specialists that I was under at the time.

I was placed on many other waiting lists for further tests and scans for neurological or central nervous system disorders – all proving negative. I even went on special diets, eliminating certain foods and additives, as it had been suggested to me that I might be having an allergic reaction to something. By the age of twenty-six my condition had deteriorated to the point where I could no longer make sense of the English language due to the ADD being so pronounced. I thought people were deliberately winding me up when I felt like they were talking in a different language from me. I was unable to recognise family, friends or familiar people (fog state), and suffered bouts of being totally unable to speak due to stress in psychosis. On occasions when I had to dash out to see somebody, I would telephone them first, to let them know I would be fifteen minutes or so, and then arrive there three to four hours later, having been walking the streets in total oblivion. This may sound strange, but, although I had been Agoraphobic, my deteriorating health meant I wasn't compos mentis enough to feel fear anymore for the outdoors. By this time, my whole world had turned upside down and I lived my life in a fantasy world during the day, thinking that my reality was when I was asleep at night.

I had by this time attempted suicide on numerous occasions in some bizarre fashions. Once, after taking 200 Paracetamol, I was rushed to the Royal Preston Hospital where the doctors fought to get my heart going again. The doctors said I was lucky to be alive. I had developed an obsession with suicide and death. I felt so unhappy and so incredibly lonely and isolated that I had become desperate to die. I remember feeling extremely angry that I had not succeeded. I feared for my sanity and felt that taking my life would save me from going insane.

Christmas 1988 saw me admitted to the Cardiology Program's Investigation Unit at Manchester Royal Infirmary, where it was suspected that a lack of blood supply in the arteries to my brain was perhaps causing my blackouts. This is where I lost my voice. I remember the nurse in theatre asking me questions about my records. I was dumbstruck. I just couldn't get a word out. All the staff in theatre just gaped at me when the nurse asked me how I was to travel home. My brain was telling me to speak, but the words just wouldn't materialise. It was the most awesome experience I had ever encountered and was to be the beginning of my eventual breakdown; a breakdown that I feel was intermittently fluctuating into insanity. My last two days there were under twenty-four hour observation as the ward nurse told me she had saved my life when I tried jumping out of the fourth floor window, which I can't remember doing.

Although my GP tried to get me admitted to the acute ward at Whittingham Psychiatric Hospital, there had been an administrative error, so a six-month wait in psychosis ensued, with me being sedated with Largactil once again. I remember having a short visit from a local community psychiatric nurse, who confidently informed me that the proposed group psychotherapy on offer to me in hospital, would strip my life down into pieces and rebuild it. A promise which haunted me during the six month wait, but was eventually proved to be misinformed, as any stripping down and rebuilding of lives had to come from my hard work and not theirs.

I attended a number of screening assessments for the psychotherapy unit in which the senior psychotherapist asked a number of questions about my past, and when I opened up to her and told her how distraught I had become about my history of abuse, she said, "Well, you're just going to have to learn how to start trusting people". Something I had been doing too much of all my life, and had got me into the mess I was in. She said it was *my* problem because I couldn't trust people. Hearing this cold statement was the reason for my initial reservations about this place. Looking back, I should have trusted my own intuition.

June 1989 saw me admitted as an in-patient to Whittingham Hospital, where I felt safe, although still frightened of the implications. I think the biggest fear people have of being admitted to a psychiatric hospital is that they will be locked up and left there to lose their sanity.

During my mental breakdown, something died in me. Inspiration for life was no longer there. Nothing gave me pleasure any more. I had lost my will to live. Nobody could seem to reach me. Small talk infuriated me, and I referred to everyone as being "prisoners of god". Devoid of all positive feelings, I had come to the realisation that I could not get any lower – the only way had to be up.

My treatment in hospital included psychoanalytically group-orientated psychotherapy, whilst living on a self-sufficient unit (a little like a kibbutz), twenty-four hours a day with sixteen other patients. Intelligence testing was given prior to group therapy. A few weeks into therapy, I started to feel that this form of treatment was inappropriate for me, but was told that I hadn't given the programme enough time to work.

Looking back on the interview for this unit, I remember ticking the box that implied that I had difficulty in making relationships, but with hindsight, I realise that I had ticked the wrong box. Gazing from the window of my psychiatric ward that night, I wondered whether I would ever find a niche in the community again.

When in group sessions, contributing patients all tended to want to talk at the same time, hence, everybody had to fight for listening space. My life was in such a mess that I would come out with these defensive one-liners which would put the most cheerful of people in a melancholy mood. The therapists said they had never met anybody as defensive as me before in therapy.

I found the patients on this unit very disturbed, often with outbursts of insults thrown at each other – a little like the House of Commons really, although the country would be in a fine mess if they were running it! Despite most of the patients having difficulty making relationships, we were all expected to counsel each other better, which seemed rather bizarre to me, as none of us had had any counselling skills whatsoever.

One particular patient I had befriended on the ward had also shown similar manifestations of my symptoms in a mild form throughout his life, but had remissioned during his time in hospital. John, as his name is, had also spent the best part of his life wracking his brains trying to put a name to the strange symptoms that had dogged his life too. Throughout our time in therapy we often discussed our symptoms as being possibly related to Tourette Syndrome, as we had seen the Tourettes issue raised on the Phil Donahue American television show.

Although TS is defined as being neuro-biological, the presenting characteristics can be accompanied by much deeper emotional and psychiatric disorders, such as OCD and ADHD. Since these phenomena were an integral part of our Tourettes, psychotherapy was not the most appropriate form of treatment for us. So it was in our best interest to stick together to defend each other when flying insults were thrown at us, basically through misunderstandings on their part. We quickly became known as the 'double act'. As time went by, I got caught up in the idiosyncrasies of life in psychotherapy, and would yet be investing my energy in finding a diagnosis for this mystery illness at a later date.

With all these emotional disturbances in mind, I felt the need to regress into my childhood in order to analyse and come to terms with all that had happened to me. "No pain, no gain," was my mantra. Unfortunately, however, despite the theoretical approach being of the psychoanalytical nature of past, upbringing and development, they disallowed regression, not knowing the true definition of psychoanalysis. Group therapy continued for the next year, during which time I formed relationships outside of the therapy groups which assisted me greatly in terms of learning to socialise once again after having become isolated from society for so long.

During this time I studied and became conversant with many different methodological approaches to counselling, becoming rather challenging in group therapy as a result. I considered the therapy to be destructive rather than constructive, their basic philosophy being that the key to the past is all in the present and the future. In retaliation, I was accused of being 'anti-therapy'. As a response to a philosophy which I found to be repressive, I wrote in the members book, 'I am what I am now, aged twenty-six, because of what I went through when I was eighty-five'. If this philosophy were true, then this statement would make sense. All physical ailments were passed off as being psychosomatic and all in the mind. No matter what physical symptoms you had, the therapists told you to take it into the group and talk about it. One example of how this nonsense went too far was when one patient complained of severe pains in his stomach. After 'taking it to the group,' it just got worse. The following weekend he sneaked out to his doctor's in the community. His GP rushed him straight to casualty, where they diagnosed a perforated peptic ulcer. They said it could have been fatal if it had been left any longer.

Some psychotherapists have an amazing ability to play the silent game on patients, while you are waiting in desperation for some constructive feedback. They sit back in their comfy chairs amidst the deafening silence that they've created, and make you, the vulnerable patient, bow in inferiority to their super-human attitude. You feel so powerless. I'd read in some MIND (national charity for mental health) publication, that this type of therapist often thinks that the longer their patients *are* their patients, it makes them better therapists. And really the best therapists are those that can guide a client into coping with his life and to be on his way in the shortest possible time.

I soon came to terms with the fact that I was dealing with a bunch of cowboys who were in the wrong type of job. I was accused of psychiatric labelling and using jargon such as depression, frustration, anxiety, and OCD. My reply was, "Where would we be without labels?" Despite this, I felt belittled and demeaned. I am particularly interested in the psychodynamic theory and remain open-minded with regard to group therapy, seeing this as being possibly beneficial for some people, if not for me. In fact, in a 1992 survey researched by MIND, the statistics proved that two thirds of patients in psychoanalytically-oriented psychotherapy showed no benefit – one third finishing up more disturbed than they were before they started therapy. Predictably, the unit I was on closed down two years after!

In an interview with the principal psychologist before discharge, I suggested that perhaps I could be referred for one of several alternative therapies, such as hypnotherapy. This was acrimoniously rejected as being nonsense, having never worked for anybody and being totally ineffective. The possibility of me having Gilles de la Tourette Syndrome was also discounted as nonsense, because Coprolalia, the therapists said, was an imperative feature of the condition. They put all my symptoms down to attention-seeking. Other patients in the group were told to ignore me, as the psychologist said I wanted to feel more special than them. Attention, of any kind, is something all people with TS want to avoid at all costs. We are embarrassed enough with our symptoms alone, without wishing to create a scene. I don't even like a camera being pointed at me. I remember telling him to take a few Largactil and go and play on the motorway! A year later, I was informed that he had been struck off for involving himself in a relationship

Bad practice →

with one of his patients, and then abusing her.

Following discharge from hospital, I returned to my rented house in Fulwood where a tide of unhappy memories flooded back. I felt rejected by the medical profession, which seemed no longer to offer me any help. I began to be tested for diseases that I had to suggest, as my GP had exhausted all of his ideas. Correspondences went back and forth from GP to specialists, only to land back on his desk as negative … negative … negative. In fact, I have since gained access to my medical records and found that letters had been sent to specialists from my GP asking them if they would see to this 'odd lad' of a patient of his, only to receive letters back from them saying, 'I agree with you, he is rather an odd lad, isn't he?' and that, 'Christopher seems to have great difficulty in accepting the fact that there is nothing physically wrong with him, after having tested him for all the diseases known to man'. I'd heard of people slipping through the net within the medical profession, but the holes in this one were huge!

However, some time after, I saw a *QED* television documentary for the BBC focusing on a young Scottish man by the name of John Davidson, who had full-blown Tourettes. I stared in elation at this young man's symptoms, and was overwhelmed by what I thought might just be what I had been burdened with all my life. I immediately put pen to paper and wrote to the Tourette Syndrome (UK) Association in London, and was forwarded a list of Tourettes specialists at a centre of excellence whom they insisted I go and see, as I had been messed about so much by the rest of the medical profession, and to whom I could be referred by my GP.

An appointment was made for six weeks later, during which time I accessed the reference library, finding several conditions relating to motor disorders. One of these was Tourette Syndrome, and described a whole range of symptoms that can be an integral part of the condition. I identified with all of them and my opinion was later verified by a Professor AJ Lees, a consultant neurologist and one of the top Tourettes specialists at the National Hospital for Neurology and Neurosurgery in London. In July 1990, he diagnosed me as suffering from the Gilles de la Tourette Syndrome. It had been a twenty-seven-year wait for this diagnosis – but what a godsend it was. I remember crying with joy, as nurses back in the waiting room comforted me. My friend John from hospital was also diagnosed with Tourette Syndrome soon after.

Shortly after my diagnosis and the publicity I received in the media, a solicitor advised me to take legal action against the NHS, simply for having to wait so long for a diagnosis, when knowledge of TS had been accessible to the medical profession since the year 1825. Early diagnosis and treatment can often prevent all the secondary psychological problems that the TSA often have to deal with. I was given the contact number for an organisation called AVMA (Action for Victims of Medical Accidents) in London, which proceeded to start legal action for medical negligence for me. However, after six months of debate amongst the lawyers, it was decided that the failure to diagnose me within twenty-seven years was in their eyes due to ignorance rather than negligence. Unlike America, we in Britain, as yet, can't sue for having an ignorant medical profession – I sit and wait! I only know that if I had been diagnosed at the age of two, when the TS started, I would probably have had a social worker who would have ensured me having a nurturing environment in which to grow up.

After the professional clinical diagnosis, I was admitted to the National Hospital as an in-patient for a Magnetic Resonance Imaging Scan (MRI) and a Positron Emission Tomography Scan (PET). These scanners, unlike all the other tests and scans I had been given over the past years, indicated structural chemical changes in the Tourettes brain when compared to a healthy brain. Antipsychotic drugs (which are dopamine blockers) were prescribed for the tics, and antidepressants prescribed for the OCD. They produced physical improvements in the condition, although, because TS is genetic, there is still no cure as yet.

Utterly overwhelmed with joy, I started to piece my life back together like a jigsaw puzzle. I felt like a huge weight had been lifted from my shoulders, as reasons for everything fitted into place. I was, and I am, very glad to be labelled a 'Touretter'. Accusations relating to my bizarre behaviour could now be answered in terms of physical illness, rather than, madness and insanity, or – as had been suggested by various people, and priests – demon-possessed.

I desperately wished to share with my mother the pure joy I was experiencing, but, unfortunately, her reaction cast a shadow over my euphoria. My parents wouldn't come to the consultation with me, so I remember phoning them from the hospital immediately after being diagnosed. My mother's response was, "Right, OK. Well, I'd better get back to cooking the vegetables – I'm in the middle of cooking tea." So I asked her to put my father on the phone. He said, "Right, OK. Well, I'd better get back, I'm watching the snooker." My mother refused to believe in the Tourettes diagnosis, making statements such as, "I'm not gullible", "I wasn't born yesterday", "This won't wash with me", "The tics may be the result of Tourettes, but all these so called associated behaviours aren't", and "You've just been a bad lad all these years". She seemed to think that because I was now in a position to piece my life together from that diagnosis, that I somehow wanted revenge for all the years of neglect and deprivation, when the only thing I was really hoping for was to share what I thought (strangely enough) to be good news with the family and share our feelings of misunderstandings from my turbulent childhood. I hoped we could come to a better understanding of how and why we related to each other the way we did and that it would bring us all closer together.

My friends tell me that they're probably riddled with guilt, but because of their denial of having done anything wrong, I find it impossible to forgive them. My mother went on to say that, "The trouble with you is that you haven't come to terms with it yet." Yet I feel I have accepted it whole-heartedly. The difficulty I have is handling the way small-minded people ridicule people like us. It is quite easy to feel paranoid when you have Tourettes. I still get days now where I feel that someone could be having a dig at me, but I suppose that when you are seeing people imitating you in the street, you know they are taking the mickey. That's my perception. On my better days, I surprise myself with my level of assertiveness. You get all kinds of different reactions then. There are the ones that continue to mock you, the ones that feel terribly embarrassed, and the ones that feel embarrassed and then proceed to patronise you. I make allowances for them, as I think they are just slow learners at trying to show sympathy. But these days I manage to laugh in the face of adversity.

On one occasion, while attending a car boot sale with friends, it came to my notice that one of the stall-holders selling stereos was having great pleasure imitating my TS symptoms. On approaching him and asking if he realised what he was ridiculing he said, "Ridiculing? I wasn't ridiculing you. I I I I I was erm erm … boogying to my music." As there was no music playing and no electricity to play it with, I kindly suggested that next time he wanted to boogie on down, he might think of plugging the appliance in first. Noting him blush deeply, I gave him my business card and told him not to hesitate to give me a call if he wanted to be educated. With that, I walked away.

However, I am not always feeling that confident. On another occasion, at a local pub that caters for live bands, I had been socialising with a friend for most of the night whilst the band on stage had been playing. Just before starting their last song, the lead singer said, "I would like to thank everybody for coming to see us performing tonight …" Then, staring me right in the face in front of a hundred people, he said, "… especially the tall chap stood at the bar, that made it all look like an asthma attack." On such days, adversity gets the better of me. Because of the sustaining impact of my troubled childhood, it's amazing how easily ridicule can make me feel like that empty inferior child again. In retrospect now, as an adult, I realise that the biggest bullies are the ones who are the most insecure and lack self-esteem. I think it would have helped me to know that as a child.

Because of bad experiences, I am very choosy as to where I socialise, how I travel, and where I sit. If I'm on a bus, or at the cinema, I will endeavour to find a seat at the very back where nobody can see me and where I will attract as little attention as possible. If I go to a disco, for example, I prefer one that caters for more mature people, as everybody will notice my symptoms in such close proximity, and there is less chance of being ridiculed. You naturally want to suppress the symptoms, but the more energy you put into doing this, the more anxious you feel and, in turn, this makes the tics worse. It can be confusing when people stare at you – is it because you have a disability, or because they fancy you?!

The world has many undesirables, and the Tourettes sufferer is often the first person to meet them. Having people mock and ridicule Tourettes on a regular basis is the most soul-destroying experience one can ever go through. I would suggest people walk a thousand miles in our shoes before ever passing frivolous judgments. I often wonder what it is about Tourettes that people find so funny when compared to any other movement disorder – I'll never know.

The prevalence of Tourettes was once thought to be 1 in 2000 people, but the latest research has found that one in every hundred children fits the criteria of TS. Amongst others, the three main associated disorders that appear commonly with TS are: Attention Deficit Disorder (ADD), Attention Deficit Hyperactivity Disorder (ADHD), and Obsessive Compulsive Disorder (OCD). I spent years suffering from the most bizarre obsessional thoughts you could ever imagine, thoughts often resulting from, or exacerbated by, violent and sexual scenes on television.

Many TS sufferers only have the illness in a mild form and may go unnoticed with just an occasional heavy eye blink, or a flick of the wrist. Life goes on as normal for them, without any psychological problems. But the more severe Tourettes child views the rest of the world as if he were visiting it as an alien from another planet. Longing for acceptance in a world of disapproval only serves to increase the isolation of being the odd one out. You know that there is something very different about you compared with the rest of the human race, and try hard to suppress your symptoms just to feel normal. You go through every conceivable emotion as all the characteristics of complex tics, obsessions and compulsions seem unrelated to other people. Children with Tourettes instinctively know that they are different from other children, often wondering why they are not displaying the same idiosyncrasies as themselves. They can feel hated by everyone they comes across, due to all of the strange behaviours. Consequently, they often have very little self-worth and can inflict a great deal of guilt upon themselves, as I did.

Hating your Tourettes is the equivalent of hating yourself in your entirety, as all its manifestations are intertwined with the innermost parts of your personality. On the other hand, accepting Tourettes as your friend is like learning how to love your enemy. I feel this is something a sufferer has to achieve, if he or she is to come to terms with and learn how to live with the condition. Thinking back to my own childhood, if there had been a local murder, I would have worried that I might have committed it in a fog state. There isn't a day goes by when I don't analyse my behaviour, in case I've acted out compulsively. I sometimes have nightmares of being sent summonses in the post for my compulsive past.

They say that the greatest love of all is learning how to love yourself, but for a person who feels unlovable, that's far easier said than done when you're reminded of all the unwitting destruction you've left behind in your life. Sufferers can put on huge fronts when modelling themselves on 'normal' people just to feel a part of society. This only serves to increase their identity crisis. Milder cases often make impressive dancers, athletes and musicians. However, sometimes sufferers just want to be accepted in society with the condition alone, rather than feeling like they have to entertain for acceptance. I sometimes feel that the only people genuinely wishing to associate themselves with me are those with some sort of disability themselves. It is difficult when you want to impress a world that is simply not impressed with a medical condition that is misconstrued as antisocial behaviour.

My parents seemed to have great difficulty in understanding why it was so important for me to put a name to all these bizarre symptoms. I had told them that it was such a relief knowing it was a physiological disorder, rather than a psychological one. They also had difficulty understanding why being sent to a children's home should have had such an impact on my life. On one occasion, my mother even denied ever sending me there – which I find rather odd. Although, by this time, I was encouraged to go to my parents' for meals, I was not allowed to refer to, or talk about, my condition whilst there. Hence, talk was trivial and rather strained. Despite my family treating TS as a taboo subject, I feel determined to let the world know about this awesome condition.

On reflection, I see a marked lack of affection towards me from my family throughout my life. My father exhibited intense dislike for me, rubbishing me to my past neighbours and, when I was a child, resorting to physical punishment on occasion. That punishment was never tempered with any warmth, love or affection. I felt that I could never do right by him, yet was always hoping for approval. I particularly wished to make my father proud of me and, with this in mind, spent six months at school making a medicine cabinet for my parents. My father criticised the finished product, which made me eventually accept that I would always be lacking in his eyes. My father was a jealous man, disapproving of any attention shown to me by my mother, and I was consequently blamed for the breakdown of their marriage.

One year I received a birthday card from my parents which read, 'I hope you think of us sometimes'. I posted it back to them stating that I do, but only in the nightmares that I have. I now look upon them as being dead. The less I see of them, the better I feel. I still have regular nightmares about them and the children's home, which are fuelled by visiting them. So, I don't. I do feel as though I can forgive them, and would very much like to, but as they deny any part in it, I'm not going to hold my breath.

Back in my rented home, after leaving hospital, with no support from family or mental health services, I again started to regress. Memories rekindled by the house I had lived in during those lonely, isolated years held me back, tying me to the past. However, the landlord went bankrupt, which necessitated me finding alternative accommodation. The extra medical points allocated to me due to my diagnosis, meant that I now had sufficient points to apply for one of eight brand new flats in a housing estate being built in a select area of Preston by a private association. Out of five hundred applicants, I was chosen to rent one of the flats. I thought that a new life was about to start for me, one that looked beyond the past to a brighter future. The place itself was very pleasant, but some of the neighbours moved in by the Council left much to be desired. Their ridicule spelled the end of that new life. Your face just didn't fit if it was different from theirs. They taunted the disabled, gay people and ethnic minorities, and each group was forced to leave as their lives were made too uncomfortable. I even witnessed one disabled chap being rocked out of his wheelchair and punched to the ground. Every such incident was reported to the police and I was asked to keep a log of them which served as evidence in getting me rehoused.

My dustbin was repeatedly set on fire by neighbours, and wild parties led to a number of them chanting insults about my medical condition outside my flat window. Incidents such as these, together with the reappearance of an old nickname 'Noddy', meant that I was supported by the government to move yet again to a more civilised neighbourhood. The local police said it was the worst case of neighbourhood victimisation they had ever come across. After nine years of living there, and four years on a waiting list to move, I finally have a home on the outskirts of the city, where my present neighbours seem more humane.

However, once established in my, then, new home on the housing association estate, a friend informed me of a day centre staffed by psychiatric nurses from Whittingham Hospital which was being run by the Lancashire Health Authorities for people recovering from mental health problems who were still needing support. Theatre Street Drop-in Centre catered for self-referrals and I started to attend. It was here that I met Carol, with whom I became close, though platonic, friends. She had been diagnosed as having Schizophrenia and severe epilepsy. She wanted more out of the relationship than I preferred, but she thought it was because of her obesity that I felt like this. As Carol's weight was much exacerbated by her medication, she decided to come off her daily dose of Depixol, after which her condition deteriorated and she was eventually admitted to the local psychiatric department. Within the following forty-eight hours, she committed suicide, as the consultants on duty failed to attend to her needs. An inquest was undertaken shortly afterwards, but nothing constructive was ever achieved. One hundred and seventy people came to her funeral. Carol would have been the first friend to accept the Tourettes in me and accept me for who I am. She is sadly missed.

I've been dumped by more women than I care to remember, after investing much emotion into them, and have realised that it is not only jobs and accommodation that Tourettes people have difficulty in attaining. I did meet a lady called Linda four years ago, who was the very first person to ever tell me she loved me, and I was very touched by this new found affection. However, just as quickly as she came into my life, six months later, she was diagnosed with terminal cancer, and died shortly after. She was full of love, and I now miss her. Apart from Linda, it's been twenty-one years since my last serious relationship. I gave up chasing some years ago. As I never experience anybody approaching a Tourettes sufferer in social places, I'm not holding my breath. Now, I sometimes feel like I have lost the ability to love any more.

I feel as if I could never trust a woman again sufficiently to give her my whole self. I hope I'm wrong. However, I can't help the feeling of longing to hold a woman in my arms without it feeling emotionally painful, and having the compulsion to nip or squeeze her. I have since joined an introduction agency where I decided not to tell the women I was introduced to that I had Tourettes until I had met them. After initially meeting them, some of them phoned the agency and were quite cross that they had introduced them to someone with a disability. The agency and I decided they would inform all prospective profiles that I had Tourettes, and since then, I haven't had a single introduction.

Since my diagnosis, irrational explanations relating to my bizarre behaviour have flooded my mind. A whole new world has opened up for me in the light of self-knowledge. I have since had various articles in newspapers and magazines, one being the *British Medical Journal*, in which an edited version of this autobiographical account first appeared, and have been interviewed on live world radio to promote greater awareness of the condition. Ironically, I spent the following four years training part-time as a voluntary advocate in the psychiatric hospital that I once lived in. As part of my advocacy work, and the special interest I have in therapies, I am now the first person in the UK to compile a directory of alternative 'talking' treatments for my own district.

Like many other mental health service users in the UK in the early nineties, I had to be discharged from hospital when one type of therapy hadn't worked for me. This directory of talking therapies has been compiled *for* the user, *by* a user. It is hoped that people's emotional needs can now be met as soon as possible with a theoretical approach tailored to suit their individual needs.

I've now had fourteen years to piece my life back together since my breakdown, and although I feel it was the toughest thing I've experienced in my life, the second toughest thing has been recovering from it. Although it has taken that long to recover, I feel that there are secondary psychological problems that still have to be worked through. People sometimes tell me it's all right for me because I am strong, but the truth is that I wasn't always strong. As a child, I was very vulnerable and very weak. The only thing I can add is that if *I* can do it, anyone can.

On my worst days there are still times when I think, "What is it all for?" Despite having a family which lacks the basic skills to offer proper support, the one thing that keeps me going is the possibility of me having a family of my own. In sharp contrast to the very material world that we live in, I somehow feel that love from a family of my own would replace any desire for material things in my life. I love children, but on the other hand, I hate them for giving me such a hard time. They can be so cruel. Perhaps the love from my own children would fill the empty gap that has endured for so long throughout my life – a life that I feel I haven't really got without a family. My only fear would be of spoiling them terribly in contrast to the way I was brought up. I may have been robbed of my childhood, but I would hope my children could tell a different story.

I have a fear of investing in meaningful relationships any more because everything good that I've ever had has been taken away from me. I don't think that anyone is the same person after going through a major breakdown, but if there's one thing for sure, you attain tremendous insight from it. I believe that success is not where you are aiming for in life, but where you've come from. All those years, I was confused as to who I was. I've been many different people in the many different jobs and lives that I have led, but in a way, the search has helped me claim my true identity, an identity that has been difficult to attain because of all the things that are associated with TS. I am just thankful that I have been saved from ending up on the street, with no future ahead of me.

I know I must have been a handful as a child, and it is certainly no bed of roses for the family of sufferers. However, I can't help feeling rather envious of those sufferers who do receive love and support from their families. With the help and support from the Tourette Syndrome Associations around the world, more and more families are being kept together, and children are being spared from being put into children's homes, which has to be a good thing.

I feel that my most important goal is to raise social awareness, particularly amongst the caring professions, and the small-minded people that give people like us such a hard time. For this reason, I have travelled out and about, giving presentations on TS to hospitals, universities, post-graduate centres and the like. I carry an ID card around with me explaining my condition. It's amazing how many people still think that Tourettes is just the swearing disease, and part of some mental illness. There are still some doctors who won't accept that it is a neurological illness, or that it even exists! They are adamant that it is all psychological, due to bad potty training, that has permeated into adulthood.

After many years of imprisonment inside this Tourettes body that God has so dearly inflicted upon me, I might still be in the grip of its many bizarre physical manifestations, but psychologically and emotionally, I now feel confident enough to break away from these feelings of embarrassment and isolation, and share them with the rest of the world.

People often view TS sufferers as being rather weird, even freakish, but the condition is only weird to the people who are frightened of it, can't understand it, or refuse to accept its existence. The brain works in many mysterious ways, and in my opinion, TS is definitely one of the most complex, mysterious and misunderstood conditions known to man. It has become known as the most commonly misdiagnosed condition in the world, and once cured, it may open up new discoveries about other neurological, or genetic disorders.

Although I have long since come to terms with having TS, the only thing that worries me for my future is the knowledge that I have already developed osteoarthritis due to decades of shaking with motor tics. It is unhealthy to shake your head and shrug your shoulders ten thousand times a day, and although the cocktail of natural supplements that I take daily keeps most of the arthritis at bay, the top vertebra in my back is becoming increasingly painful as time goes by.

Apart from the worry of my arthritis, I didn't think it was ever possible to feel as emotionally well as I feel now, and my present friends often ask me what therapy has helped me recover from my breakdown the most. Well, as I'd exhausted all my old coping strategies prior to my breakdown, I've had to learn a whole new set to survive into the future. I've found it important to set myself limited goals, no matter how small – day-to-day tasks that I must fulfil to ensure my well-being and bring back my self-worth and self-esteem. Ultimately, I am striving for that big goal – recovery.

If there is one thing I learned throughout my time in psychotherapy, it is that you can't change the world, which is something I think I was trying to do prior to therapy, and which was contributing to my unhappiness at the time. Instead, I have learned that you have to change yourself, and the way you feel about the world you live in. But without the dedicated support from the TSA (UK) and its members, just being there for me, writing my story wouldn't have been possible. Put all these factors together over a period of time, and that time can be the best healer of all. If, however, there was a neuro-biological cure tomorrow, I feel I would never be psychologically cured, as the mental scars lie too deep. So, for the meantime, I'll settle for the pride of my sanity and belief in MYSELF.

It is with this in mind that I dedicate this autobiographical account, not only to all Tourettes sufferers, but to the carers as well, in the hope that this story will help prevent any sufferer going through what I have had to endure. Tourettes is a life sentence for anyone unfortunate enough to suffer from it, which is why I decided to title my story, 'Life' for Tourettes.

In March 1994, I was asked to join the TSA (UK) Executive Committee and gladly accepted, and now assume a vital role in directly representing the views of those with the disorder. I feel that sharing knowledge of the complications and associated prejudices of Tourettes, can help families overcome many psychological problems.

For the first time in my life, I feel privileged to belong to an association that accepts me for who I am. Below is my life – in brief – in poetry.

An edited testimonial version of this autobiography was published in the *British Medical Journal* in October 1996.

DESTINY'S PLAN

Within these walls I sit and wait.
Are fear and torment to be my fate?
Childhood memories mock and cry,
This life I lead is all a lie,

Deviant, cruel, is this really me?
Is the bleakness there for all to see?
As faceless I hide and cower from sight,
Turning inward from the light.

Yet destiny's plan is not to choose.
The path is set to win, not lose.
Summoning all my strength to see
And reach out to find the real me.

So take my life – a jewel rare –
If this will show others how to care.
That with understanding they might see
Through to the spirit of others like me.

Chris Mansley

highlight the condition

↑
another

Problems of acceptance & understanding in society

bad behaviour = rehoming
abuse @ work

Problems of limited GP understanding.
↳ ignorance, blind, Superiority complex's, Mal Practice

ONE DAY AT A TIME

Graham Baker's Story by his Mum, Kim

I remember when Graham was born, weighing eight and a half pounds, a beautiful baby boy. I had an overwhelming sense of love, which was extra special, because I was convinced I'd have a girl. Now I had one of each, Graham, and little Lynsey who was nineteen months old. Graham had arrived two weeks before his expected time. He was delivered naturally, without painkillers, as my experience with Lynsey had put me off any intervention. Things ran smoothly and before we knew it, we were back home.

We had no problems with Graham. He slept well, fed well, and reached all the milestones normally. However, he was a quiet child who didn't mix well. He'd even shy away from close members of his family. We assumed he'd grow out of it. He never had many illnesses, apart from chicken pox.

When Graham started school, he was still very quiet. On the estate where we lived children would call for him, but he never wanted to step out of the door. On rare occasions he would venture out, but quickly come back home. This was when our problems began. In the morning it would take him ages to get dressed. I would say, "Graham, get dressed!" and I'd put his clothes in front of him every morning, always on the same chair. He seemed oblivious to this and would ask, "Where are my clothes?" I'd just spent ten minutes pushing to get him washed and dressed, showing him yet again where his clothes were. Every morning was the same.

When we spoke to Graham we had to repeat things over and over again, until we got his attention and managed to make him listen. We thought he must have a hearing problem, but when his hearing was tested it was fine. So we thought maybe he was just ignoring us. This went on for a few years.

Teachers started to comment about his withdrawn behaviour. His work was slow and deliberate, and often work set for him was not finished. His letters had to reach the top line, and he wasn't doing very well at reading. I would try and get him to sit on my knee while I read him stories, but he showed no interest at all. I was concerned and started to spy on him in the school playground, worried that he'd be alone. He was often walking around on his own, with his head down. When Graham was nine I spoke to the teacher about his poor progress in reading, but she said that he would catch up eventually.

Time and time again teachers would complain that Graham, "... just looks straight through you" and at home he was happy to let the world pass by. Children stopped calling for him, fed up with being turned away. I tried to encourage him to go out, but it didn't work. His form teacher suggested keeping him in his class for another year, commenting that he was a quiet child and had spoken no more than two sentences to him in the past year.

He asked if I wanted Graham to see a child psychologist. I was horrified and would have none of it. I wasn't about to put labels on my son. I thought that as he got older he would get better. Looking back, it was the worst thing I could have done, ignoring it. But after all, I was so used to Graham's behaviour, I didn't see what other people saw. Maybe I was in denial.

My second daughter, Loren, was then born and I had my own little family. She started nursery and was a very bright child. Lynsey, the eldest, was at school and doing very well.

Unfortunately, my children's father and I split up. I explained to them that instead of having one home now, they would have two. Their father never lost contact and the weekly routine is still the same, even to this day. The weekdays they spend with me, and the weekends they stay with their father and their grandma and grandad. I am still close friends with their father and class his family as mine, and the children took it all in their stride.

My children and I moved into a new area and they settled into their new schools. It didn't take long for Graham to be noticed. They said that although he was a loner, he was popular and his classmates were protective towards him. Things at home were still the same, always having to tell him to get dressed over and over again.

Suddenly I noticed him blinking a lot, and his grandma and grandad commented on it, too, but we just put it down to habit. Then Graham developed a thing about sleeping on the floor. He said he liked it because it was hard. He began to store food and toys under his quilt, and curl up in a ball with his quilt over his head and sleep like that. He did the same at his father's house and on Sundays he and I would talk to each other about Graham's strange behaviour. But I grew really concerned one day when I saw Graham taking his socks and shoes on and off repeatedly. Also his blinking had become worse and he was now screwing up his face. We took him to a doctor to have his eyes and ears tested, but everything seemed fine.

Eventually, though, his father and I took him again to the doctor to ask for help. Graham was due to go to secondary school after the holidays and I knew he would not be able to cope. The doctor put his name down to see an educational psychologist. Graham did go to the comprehensive school but it was a nightmare for him. He wouldn't eat or speak and said that he wanted to kill himself. I watched my son crumble, his life fell apart in front of us. We were at a loss as to what to do. His headteacher said, "It's as if he's in a world of his own."

Then Graham refused to go to school. We tried everything, even physically carrying him into the car to get him there. He would not get on the school bus because he was really anxious about sitting next to anyone, and when forced, he would squat in the middle of the gangway, drawing more attention to himself. The psychologist came to see him at home and at school. Graham had seen her several times by now, but would not even acknowledge her, often hiding underneath the table. She explained that he was not coping at all and that she was very concerned.

By now, I was completely bewildered. Graham's behaviour got even worse. He developed a compulsion to straighten everything. The psychologist told me that she suspected that Graham might have Autism, and brought along a colleague who worked with autistic children. When they arrived, her colleague spent over an hour doing puzzle tests with Graham, and asking questions about his feelings. Graham could not answer the questions but he was excellent at doing the puzzles. His father and I had spent hundreds of pounds on Tecnic, and he would build robots, spaceships, and aeroplanes, which all involved very fine detail. He didn't need any help. He excelled in such things.

When the visit ended, it was explained that Graham was autistic, but that he had a mild form of it called Asperger's. His father and I were shocked, but at least it explained his behaviour, except that by now he was plucking invisible objects out of the air, and raising his arms in the air and having difficulty getting them down again.

When our relationship with the children's unit began, it was a trying time for us, for in order to assess Graham, he had to stay as a residential patient. But we knew he was in good hands. The weeks turned into months and they were worried, at one point, that he might be psychotic. I didn't even know what this meant. Finally, his co-worker got through to him and he opened up slightly.

At weekends he would spend one night with me and one night with his father, but this was stressful. He continued plucking things from the air, taking a long time to get dressed, and touching walls and door frames, etc. But these things didn't become noticeable at the unit for four or five months. Eventually, it became evident that he was touching walls, stooping to touch his feet, and patting the floor. He was still behind with his schoolwork, but we were pleased that he was now joining in on school outings. He came home after about eight months.

However, the unit staff agreed with us that he would not fit into comprehensive school, so he was sent to a special needs school. We did ask Graham's consultant what was wrong, and were amazed at his reply. "Why? Why ask why, why, why? Sometimes these things happen. The brain is very complex." Like little children we were sent away with no answers and were left feeling useless.

The special school was the best thing that had ever happened to Graham, although, at first, he would often miss the transport laid on for him. It took around six weeks to get him used to the routine, but after that it was worth it. His schoolwork improved and he began to mix better. His confidence improved by leaps and bounds, and I knew he was happier when he started to burst through the door like a time bomb, and he became really chatty. But the worst was yet to come.

Graham started sniffing again, and continually blowing down his nose like a steam train. We found it very difficult to cope with, and daren't sniff ourselves in case it set him off. The continual noise, from the moment he woke up, put us all on edge all the time. My other children were affected, especially when he blew everything out of his nose, and when he sniffed he patted himself, and he would reach out, and would run to touch the walls, and when he walked, he hurried, then would very suddenly stop still.

I wondered if, maybe, this was Parkinson's disease. Suddenly Graham seemed happy to talk for hours, but only on one subject. We would tell him that we had moved on and were talking about something else, but it was as if he was stuck in a groove and couldn't stop. He became obsessive about his food. It had to be checked, and if his plate was touched after his meal was served, he would leave the whole thing, saying that we had done something to it.

One day I picked up a children's ailment book, and as I browsed through the pages I saw the word tics, and I realised that Graham did these things, but all over his body. As I read further, a more severe form of tics was described, called the Gilles de la Tourette Syndrome. I couldn't believe my eyes. The book was describing Graham. So I bought it. It cost 99p.

I saw the psychologist again and told him what I had read. But he said that people with Tourettes cannot control it, and they swear. He was extremely doubtful about the condition in Graham's case but agreed to ask the doctor to refer him to a specialist, so that it could be confirmed one way or the other. He said that the specialist would know. At the time we thought the specialist would be a Tourettes expert, but, in fact, he was a neurologist. Graham, his father, and I all went to the hospital. The specialist asked about our family history and about his past, about his movements and how they first started. He examined Graham and noticed some small sniffs. We were with him for about half an hour. Finally, he told us that, yes, our son did have Tourette Syndrome. I asked him if he was certain, and he said, "Yes, one hundred per cent."

Later, when the diagnosis came through the post, we felt that a great weight had been lifted off our shoulders. Now Graham would have help.

on. Relief.

Grasp understanding.

The specialist told us that he didn't want to prescribe drugs because of their side effects, but would try Graham on relaxation. We were so relieved, because we knew that Graham didn't do any of these strange things on purpose. But we were sent away and told to return in six months. That was when I joined the Tourettes Association. But still, very difficult times lay ahead.

We took Graham to the adolescent unit expecting him to receive treatment, now that we knew what the problem was. But, again, it seemed that he would need to stay as a resident so that he could be assessed again, and we had to agree, reluctantly. But how else would he get help? The same questions were asked. We'd done this before. We were back to square one. Graham spent the week there, as before, and weekends at home. Our lives seemed so normal, easy and peaceful, that it was like a little bit of heaven. But the unit reported that Graham did nothing unusual.

We tried to explain how he would hide his symptoms and do them when he was alone, in his bedroom, the bathroom, etc, and that when he came home at weekends his sniffs and touches were much worse. Family meetings were held and we would describe the weekend's events, and then Graham was questioned and gave all the wrong answers. So then we had to further explain that Graham found it hard to take everything in when he was highly stressed, and we'd explain what was happening over and over to him until he seemed to understand. But then the following week we'd have to go through the whole thing again.

Eventually Graham had to leave the adolescent unit because we were asked to send him daily instead of weekly, and we couldn't do that. With our work commitments it was impossible, and we knew that Graham would never cope with the bus journeys alone. My son is a bright boy, but he would get anxious and panic if things didn't go exactly to plan, so it was out of the question. We agreed, however, to attend with Graham at regular intervals.

The unit advised us to get as much evidence as possible, because it would help Graham. So we made tapes and took them to our first appointment with a consultant, but it was obvious that this man had already made up his mind. He explained his fascination with the fact that Graham had displayed no symptoms while residing at the unit, or at school, only at home. He then suggested that Graham should live elsewhere, "just as an option". His father and I were shocked. He was our son and we loved him. We explained that Graham did these things in both our homes, and that possibly he did this because he was more relaxed when with his family, and that he always hid his symptoms from people he didn't know because of embarrassment, both for himself and for others. We told him that Graham would do these things when he was alone, and that perhaps they hadn't watched him carefully enough, but the answer to that was a knowing smile, and then he said, "Maybe Graham has a hidden anger inside him. Maybe he was affected by your splitting up years ago."

We explained that it had been an amicable split and that we still had a close relationship. We told him that we wanted Graham to be treated for Tourette Syndrome, and that we now felt that things had gone round in circles and we were no further on. His only advice was that we enter family therapy, because maybe the problem was down to how we interacted with each other. As I played the tape, he spoke over it. I switched it off and we left the meeting in shock. How could a professional man speak like that? By the time we arrived home I was devastated. I began to question myself. Maybe I'd chastised Graham too much over the years. Had I made him a nervous wreck? Had Graham resented the parting between his father and me? I couldn't cope with these feelings. I was in tears and felt that I couldn't go on.

I told the psychologist what had happened. I was distraught that anyone could even think of our son living anywhere but at home. He told me that he had been at a meeting two weeks earlier, when it was reported that the unit staff had witnessed some of Graham's strange behaviour, and that he himself had witnessed it inside our home. So why didn't the consultant have this information?

That is how I came to write my story. I telephoned Chris Mansley at the Tourettes Association. Chris put everything into perspective and I learned a great deal from him. I felt ready again to fight on, knowing that I was not alone any more. It was great to speak to someone who suffered from Tourettes himself, and I realised that I was speaking to a man who had come through a great deal and who had had to do it without help from anyone. Here was an intelligent, articulate and strong young man. If he could get through this, then so could my son and our family.

Nevertheless, life at home now seemed in shreds and I cried most days. I saw my doctor for some support and asked him to speak to a Tourettes specialist. He said he was unable to help and gave me the number of the Health Authority, for apparently, if I wanted Graham to be treated outside the area then I had to contact them myself. I explained to him that Graham needed support and treatment, and received in return the suggestion that I seek psychiatric help for myself. I turned this down. He explained that he liked to deal with quick medical matters, and that since Tourettes was very rare (which it is not), it was not possible for him to help. I left the surgery in tears. But I rang the Health Authority and was told that my doctor was wrong in not ringing them himself to find a specialist, and that I would be wise to change doctors if he continued to refuse to help me. They told me to go back to him and ask that he refer Graham to a doctor at St James'

Hospital in Leeds who actually dealt with Tourettes.

I rang my doctor again but had to explain everything to the receptionist who was very abrupt and spoke to me as if I was complaining. She said she would tell the doctor what I had said, but when I asked when I could expect an appointment, I was told, "When you get an appointment card through your door". I told her that this wasn't good enough, that Graham needed immediate help and I needed to know quickly if the doctor was willing to refer Graham to Leeds. I was so distressed by all this that I rang the Health Authority again. They took over and contacted my doctor, pointing out that there was no reason why he should continue to refuse extra help for Graham since we lived in the East Riding area anyway, and also pointed out to him that everyone was entitled to a second opinion. This worked wonders and he agreed to refer Graham to the Tourettes specialist at St James'. Thank God. I then took Graham out of the adolescent unit.

But I spent many sleepless nights questioning myself. Had I neglected my son and abused him without realising it? Did we have a family problem? I even began to wonder whether or not I should even shout at him when he misbehaved. Our world was turning upside down. Even more so when talking to Chris Mansley TSA (UK) again, for I was told that the doctor in Leeds was not actually a Tourettes specialist. However, Chris recommended one from a list that the Tourette Syndrome Association have. His name was Dr Hugh Rickards in Birmingham. I decided to take this list to my son's neurologist who had first diagnosed Tourettes, and he was disappointed that Graham had not received proper treatment at the adolescent unit, and he agreed to refer Graham to Dr Rickards. So all we had to do now was wait.

My son is now fifteen and a fine looking boy. He is much taller than me and almost as tall as his father. His odd behaviour continues and he does many strange things now. They change from time to time. His latest one is bending down to touch the floor with his nose. At times he walks like a soldier, backward and forward, then sideways. He can suddenly go rigid and be unable to move for several seconds. He swipes his fingers across the cooker flames and turns the gas knobs on and off repeatedly. We have to watch him as he makes hot drinks, for his arm might suddenly move up and down whilst pouring tea. But he still helps me prepare meals, although this can be stressful because he can grab my hand while I am stirring something. For a few months he would eat nothing but fish, and now he refuses to drink tea or coffee because of the caffeine. He watches my every move and I have to wash my hands over and over again, and he gets distressed if he sees something he doesn't like, a knife, perhaps, that he thinks isn't clean enough.

Reading about Tourettes has helped me enormously. Now I know that

Graham isn't being cheeky when he repeats things I've just said, and that when he shouts, "Stupid idiot!" out of the blue, he doesn't mean to offend. We ignore these remarks and see the funny side. But he will be relentless in teasing his baby sister, reducing her to tears. These are the times when the strain shows and I need my own space, usually half an hour in the bath. I call it my, "feeling sorry for myself time". I recommend it, because after a good cry, I'm ready to soldier on.

My son, his father and I, all travelled down to Birmingham. We were nervous, afraid that we might meet the same attitudes as before. All we wanted was an acknowledgment of our son's condition. But we had no need to worry. The atmosphere was totally different. Dr Rickards listened and spoke to Graham and to us, and he knew the right questions to ask. For the first time Graham was able to explain how he felt. He was able to describe how uncomfortable he became if he was not able to do the strange things he did, and the relief he felt when he did them. The appointment lasted a couple of hours, and Dr Rickards diagnosed him with Tourette Syndrome and with Asperger's. He advised that we should also join the Autistic Association. He explained how important it was to get the right diagnoses. This was vital in order to get the right treatment for Graham.

By a chance conversation I found another family whose little boy was diagnosed with Tourette Syndrome and Attention Deficit and Hyperactivity Disorder (ADHD). It was good to meet someone who understood. We could support each other and pass on information. She advised me to seek the help of social workers, and although I was reluctant, I have found them to be a great help. They are part of the Barnardo's Children's Disability team in Hull, and I am so pleased to have their support.

We now know we are heading in the right direction and that there is light at the end of the tunnel. To anyone who might be in my position and reads my story, I would say that the most important step is to educate yourself and read as much as you can. This will stand you in good stead for the long and difficult journey ahead. Now we take one day at a time. After many years of doubt and panic, which so rocked Graham's world, I truly know that we all love Graham. We will all stand by him, his sisters too, and he will get the treatment that will improve his life immensely. In doing this, Graham will know how much we all love and care for him. We will never let him down. He deserves it.

Many thanks to Chris Mansley for listening, to Graham's school in Northcott, to my family and friends for their encouragement and to the Barnardo's Children's Disability Team.

WHY ME?

John Bradshaw

Two very important dates in my life – 21 March 1969 and 15 October 1990. The first being my date of birth, the second, when I was diagnosed with Tourette Syndrome. Yes, twenty-one years of wondering, waiting, frustration, suffering, emotional pain, panic and anxiety. Appalling, unusual, surprising, worrying – maybe all of these, but twenty-one years is a long time to wait for a clinical diagnosis, whichever way you look at it.

My mother had a difficult birth with me, and I was not breathing properly because my bronchial tubes were congested with mucus and blocked. Could the lack of oxygen have contributed to the fact that I developed Tourette Syndrome, as there is no one in my immediate family who has TS, and none of my long deceased relatives either? So where did it come from?

I first believed I was different from other children at the age of five, when I had strange thoughts such as the urge to hurt myself, utter strange phrases, vocalise my strange thoughts, destroy things, and touch things obsessively such as cars, walls, fences, people, animals, etc. Everything I did had to be done by numbers. For example, I had to walk from say one lamp-post to the next in say thirty seconds, in thirty steps. It was frustrating. I was being controlled by something in my body which was alien to me. I did not want to do it – so why was I doing it? Were other children the same? Did adults do this? Did other people exhibit this type of behaviour? I was very much alone – how does a young child explain to an adult what is going on in his mind? I definitely did not feel normal. I knew there was something wrong with me, even at the age of five or six, so I developed a type of structure to help with my odd behaviour and strange thoughts. It got me through the day but, more importantly, it helped me behave and act with others as if there was nothing wrong with me – a very difficult task given the complexities of TS.

Okay – so what is Tourette Syndrome? Tourette Syndrome is a neuro-biological condition often mistaken for a psychological illness. Symptoms include facial grimaces and involuntary spasmodic body movements called tics, which can vary in severity. Sufferers often have involuntary vocal sounds such as yelping, barking and screaming, often disguising these noises by pretending that they are clearing their throat. Confirmatory, but not essential for diagnosis, is involuntary swearing, repeating the words of others, obsessive and compulsive ritualistic behaviour (urges that cannot be controlled, but control you, best describe the condition). Associated behaviours of Tourette Syndrome are hyperactivity – ADHD – difficulty with concentration, failure to complete one task before shifting to the next, not listening, being easily distracted, acting before thinking and general boredom, fidgeting and unease. Learning disabilities and impulse control difficulties are also apparent. Unfortunately, luck never being my forte, I suffer from the lot! I now can treat TS with some humour because if I did not, I would definitely have had a nervous breakdown. I must admit though, I prefer other people to treat both me and my Tourettes seriously, as I sometimes feel that ignorant people are laughing *at* me rather than *with* me.

Starting nursery school at the age of four at Northlands, in Blackpool, was rather uneventful, as far as me and my Tourettes went, as it was only around this time that I began to realise that something was wrong with me. When I progressed to Arnold Preparatory School, a private school, at the age of five, I first experienced the urge to destroy. A simple task for an ordinary person such as painting a picture presented itself with complex problems for me as I had the urge, or compulsion, to pour paint on myself, on the floor, all over the picture, screw up the paper, or even rip it in half. This caused me a lot of severe anxiety, as I really did not want to do it – so why was I doing it?

This problem still persists, and writing this résumé of my life down on paper is presenting severe difficulties for me and this simple task takes me fifty times longer than it would for a non-sufferer. A further problem associated with writing is the compulsion to either snap the pen, or throw it to the other side of the room. To overcome this I have to keep stopping and leaving the room until the compulsion becomes less severe, and this is one of the reasons it takes me so long. Reading a book presents similar problems. How can a five-year-old child realise that they do not want to do the destructive things they are doing? But I did realise. Writing an essay at school presented the aforementioned problems. My teachers told me off constantly for having thin note books, as when I needed to write in them I had the compulsion to scribble and cross out what I had written, necessitating me to tear out the damaged pages. This compulsion kept repeating itself. I could not explain to my teachers why I had to keep doing it, as I knew they would not understand. I was warned I would get detention if I continued to do it – but continue I did. Defiant I hear you say, no – compulsive. I really could not help or control what I was doing, the urge to destroy things was so strong, as was the anxiety I suffered if I did not comply with my own strange demands upon myself.

Luckily for me, at this stage in my life, I did not suffer from involuntary vocal noises. These became apparent later in my childhood, at about the age of thirteen or so. My years in prep school between the ages of five and about eight, were not really too bad, considering, as a lot of my obsessive thoughts remained just that – thoughts – thankfully. But even so, in my early years I was bullied due to my odd behaviour and mild tics. This may have been because at school I was somewhat timid and would not answer back, or defend myself. In total contrast, at home I took my built-up frustration and emotional pain from being bullied, out on my parents, as it felt safe to do so. Life for my parents must have been very difficult due to my behaviour, temper tantrums and hyperactivity. I remember once 'going on strike' at home, refusing to eat proper, wholesome food, and instead only eating chocolate mini rolls and drinking orange squash – which further exacerbated my condition, due to the food additives contained therein.

I left Arnold Preparatory School for Arnold Junior School when I was about eight, and this is when I noticed my TS getting considerably worse. I struggled through three years of junior school with some of the most difficult, devastating, destructive and dangerous compulsions you could possibly imagine. As an example, when cutting with scissors I had the urge to throw them in the air and stand underneath them as they came down, only jumping out of the way at the last minute. I suffered the same urges when using sharp items such as knives, shears and the like. Also, when using a knife in craft class, I had the urge to cut myself with it. This I never acted upon.

At the age of eleven I went on to Arnold Senior School. By now I had started to develop twitches, or tics. The type of tic (fast, rapid, jerky movements of the body) I developed involved my head and neck, and I would thrust my head forward and upwards, somewhat like the head movement of a pigeon or a duck, which caused great humour for a lot of the pupils (particularly a select handful) and consequently they would imitate, mock and ridicule me. This is when the real bullying began. I felt I had no one to turn to, as how could I explain my bizarre behaviour to an adult, relative, or teacher when I concealed or controlled it, and everyone thought that to all intent and purposes I was a normal child with a strange habit? Tourette Syndrome in the 1970s was relatively unheard of, and only became apparent to me in about 1985, during the constant search for a name for my illness. It was also embarrassing for me to confide in someone, and still is, but to a much lesser extent nowadays as TS and ADHD is more widely recognised and known, and maybe, hopefully, in some circles accepted and understood. My years in senior school (1980-1986) were sheer hell due to my destructive compulsions, ADHD and daydreaming. I once remember a teacher saying to me, "Why don't you just leave school now and join the dole queue?" Another wrote in my report that, 'John appears to be on the planet at which he is staring through the window'. These comments did nothing for my confidence and self-esteem, which was already low.

Looking back, I have great confidence in myself and high self-esteem because I realise just how much I achieved despite my learning difficulties – going on to attain eight O Levels with good grades and to study Geography/Geology, Law, Economics, Psychology and General Studies at A Level, which unfortunately I had to pack in due to the stress, strain and trauma suffered at school as a direct and indirect result of my TS. I also excelled at swimming, gaining many qualifications in life saving, becoming the swimming team captain, representing North Lancashire and competing in national swimming competitions around the UK. I also swam outdoors, completing swims such as Lake Windermere in Cumbria and the River Wharfe in Yorkshire. My sister was also a swimmer and swam the English Channel in 1979 from England to France in ten hours, nine minutes. She was just fifteen years old. I also wanted to do this swim, but due to the pressure of my illness I had to decline. Here again, in my swimming career, I ceased to participate due to the aforementioned pressures.

Going back to my school work again; because of my difficulties in writing, I could not complete a written sentence due to my constant compulsive crossing out and scribbling on the paper, which necessitated me doing my homework during my spare time at school, because if I wrote an essay in front of someone, I could control the compulsive urges to destroy due to my 'friends' (in inverted commas because they were not real friends, just people I considered I knew, but who did not really know me) watching me, and it would therefore have been embarrassing for me to act out my destructive urges. This was my strategy to enable me to complete homework. I remember the class once received a hundred lines, which my sister had to do for me.

During my childhood years my mother realised that there was something not quite right with me, and tried to get me medical help, but to no avail, possibly due to my reluctance to tell all and the ignorance of the medical profession. One social worker once suggested to my mother that I would be better off in care – an offer she rejected. The family carried on trying to cope with me in what they considered to be the best way possible, and I continued to see various doctors, but my condition still went undiagnosed for the reasons mentioned. Considering what had been told to the doctors both by my parents and myself, they should have realised something was amiss and maybe referred me to a specialist who had more knowledge in this field of adolescent behaviour.

I was picked on greatly at school, both physically and verbally, to such an extent that I was afraid to attend, and would invent any excuse to stay at home. An early diagnosis and an explanation about my behaviour to teachers may have prevented this bullying. No one who has not been in the same situation can begin to realise or understand what a dreadful feeling of fear and intrepidation I felt on going to school. Sometimes it was so bad I was physically sick. An early diagnosis would therefore have been a godsend. Not only did the pupils pick on me, but also the teachers. My football teacher even ridiculed me for my lack of participation and poor ability in football lessons and made me want to miss soccer periods. I felt terrible. I constantly felt fearful, anxious and stressed. Because I was receiving criticism from an adult, I felt that if I confided in another adult about my difficulties and worries the reply would have been, "Pull your socks up and stick up for yourself. Don't be so weak". So I didn't say anything.

Even getting dressed to go to school was distressing, because once dressed (which took ten times longer than any other person, due to constant checking that my clothes were actually on), I experienced the compulsion to rip my clothes and destroy them. One item of clothing on to which I directed a lot of my compulsive energy, was my tie. I kept ripping it off, which necessitated my mother having to virtually dress me every morning up to a late age, about fourteen years old. Once someone else had dressed me, I felt I was not at liberty to undo their work. You see, all my destructive urges were directed towards myself and my property – not other people's.

My problems at school, what with being bullied and the anxiety and stress I suffered as a direct result, compounded with trying to control my Tourette Syndrome, made me feel physically ill, which in turn caused frustration and made me badly behaved at home, and unfortunately my parents suffered the brunt of this. At home I became a very naughty child. Some of this was just normal bad behaviour, somewhat expected from a young child, and some was TS behaviour. Such are the complexities of TS that it is virtually impossible to distinguish between the two. Hence, my parents constantly reprimanded me. At the time, I resented being punished because I thought, as a child does, "I can't help my behaviour, I can't control what I am doing. I don't want to behave like this – so why am I being told off?" With benefit of hindsight and knowing what I know now, I realise the frustration and anger they must have endured by saying, "Don't do this. Don't do that. Stop it!" etc, and me compulsively carrying on as if in complete and utter defiance. The more 'defiant' I was, the more I was punished, and a vicious circle of naughty behaviour – punishment – more naughty behaviour was established. I grew up really beginning to believe that my name was 'Stop it'! The more I was punished, the naughtier I became, and the more resentment I built up against my parents.

As I said before, knowing what I know now, I have no axe to grind with my parents. I say now to all parents of possible Tourettes sufferers reading this – if your child is naughty, or exhibits odd or strange behavioural patterns, STOP – count to ten – and ask your son or daughter, "Please try and be good. Do you really want to behave like this?" You may then get a very favourable answer that can be worked upon. It may just work, and also relieve a lot of stress and tension within the family.

At this time in my life I had suddenly developed my own language. If I was asked a question, or spoken to by my parents, I would answer in my own peculiar words that sounded like a foreign language. This frustrated my parents no end, and went on for many years. I think people thought I was just being stupid and awkward. They didn't realise that it wasn't awkwardness, it was compulsive, and I really couldn't help it.

I carried on seeing various doctors but my condition was baffling. A common response was, "He's just looking for attention", "A personality disorder", "It's just a phase he's going through", so my parents and I just soldiered on, none the wiser.

I left school at the age of nearly seventeen, having decided I could no longer cope with the pressure, which was a shame really because, not being modest, I am a very intelligent, articulate, responsible person. Soon after leaving school (four weeks in fact) I obtained employment in the Civil Service, which only made my TS worse, because the job I was doing was very repetitive and involved checking and putting into numerical order stamped certificates. As I suffered from a lot of checking compulsions anyway, I became very anxious, and this made it difficult for me to move on to my next batch of work, as I kept repeating myself. During my years of employment in the Civil Service I continued to see doctors, but to no avail.

Eventually I was signed off by my doctor with 'nervous debility'. I went to see a psychiatrist who diagnosed me with a personality disorder and thereafter I was referred to a psychotherapy unit in Blackpool where I stayed for approximately three to four months. The therapeutic regime included group therapy which involved talking about your problems with other patients, supervised by a psychotherapist. This type of therapy was useful for people who suffered from emotional and social problems, and relationship difficulties. With TS, you do suffer from these, but they are secondary psychological problems and will only respond to therapy once the underlying cause has been treated satisfactorily. I was told I was not putting any effort in and that was why the therapy was ineffective for me. My response to this was to comment that, if your car has an engine fault, you take it to a garage for advice and repair, not a florist! Many informed me that I was stubborn and anti-therapy and would not give therapy a chance to work. I felt no one was prepared to listen to my feelings and my thoughts as to why it could not possibly work until the underlying cause of my psychological problems had been investigated. I felt that these few months in therapy did absolutely nothing for me.

Tourette Syndrome does give you secondary psychological and emotional problems as mentioned earlier, which can be helped by psychotherapy, but first the illness has to be diagnosed and treated. Once this has been done, psychotherapy may be of some limited use to a TS sufferer. I left this unit and my parents took me to see a private psychiatrist who basically said the same as my previous psychiatrist and referred me to yet another psychotherapy unit, this time at an in-patient unit in Preston. I stayed here for approximately a year. However, even before I arrived I realised that this type of therapy was not right for me, and after just one week on the unit, I was one hundred per cent sure that it was not correct, but I stayed just so that no one could accuse me of not trying.

The first day I arrived on the unit I noticed one of the patients had severe head tics and spasmodic body movements, which I instantly recognised to be Tourette Syndrome. Chris, as his name was, said that he felt rather uncomfortable with the visual attention I was focusing on him. About an hour after the group ended I approached him to tactfully discuss his affliction. I mentioned Tourette Syndrome and he said he believed he had it. I told him all about myself and how I considered that I also had TS. We formed a strong bond of friendship and often during therapy both patients and therapists accused us of being an anti-therapy double act!

During my year on the unit I formed a couple of intimate personal relationships with the opposite sex, which came to nothing, due to their emotional disturbances. I have to admit that my year in therapy was somewhat beneficial, as I did learn a reasonable amount about myself and my personality, and used this information to become a less aggressive, more relaxed, sociable and interactive person. Due to the depth of the disturbance of many of the other patients, there were many outbursts and plenty of insults exchanged during group therapy, benefiting no one really. I found it hard to concentrate on this unit and was constantly switching from one topic to the other due to my ADHD, although it was not accepted that such a condition existed.

Even to date, many doctors are still in conflict with each other as to the actual existence of ADHD – in my view, a totally unacceptable state of affairs. During my years in therapy and visits to the doctor, I also developed a sun intolerance skin condition (Solar Urticaria) and am now the proud owner of two syndromes, which further made it difficult to cope, due to my inability to go outdoors during daylight hours. If I did, I would instantly get a vivid red skin rash (severe prickly heat) all over, because of the weak tolerance of my skin to the sun's rays. This further reduced my confidence and self-esteem. I became very depressed and withdrawn and would spend a lot of time on my own, making it difficult for me to form relationships. All my negative feelings of depression, anxiety, pain and panic were now showing themselves in the form of anger, which I directed at other people.

I discharged myself from the Psychotherapy Unit at Whittingham and was referred to a Tourette Syndrome centre of excellence by my GP, as by this stage I considered that I was definitely suffering from TS. This was the National Hospital for Neurology and Neurosurgery in London. My referral was aided by support from my parents, as I was unable to cope by myself. It was in 1990 that Professor AJ Lees, a top TS specialist, finally diagnosed me. It was a godsend, and I remember my appointment distinctly because I was physically unable to speak due to the stress and panic I suffered, both from being in public and the embarrassment of having to verbalise my compulsions to a stranger. I had to write everything on paper for him to read and eventually broke down crying.

I spent a week in the National Hospital having various tests and brain scans and was then referred to a hospital in Beckenham in Kent that specialised in treating people with Obsessive Compulsive Disorder (OCD). By this time my OCD was dreadful. It was taking me five to six hours to dress, and between one and two hours to leave the house due to constant checking that the door was closed, gas taps off and the like. That's the thing with OCD; rationally, you know that the gas *is* off, doors *are* locked, but you still feel the need to double check to alleviate the anxiety. It's as though you've forgotten whether the door is actually locked or not the moment you have locked it, and it feels like a distant memory. Still nobody was fully aware of what I had to cope with. I spent quite a while in the Kent hospital and unfortunately it was not of much help as my OCD was neurological (clinical) and part of my TS, whereas other patients' OCD was reactive, that is, it had developed as a reaction to a stressful period in their life. This can happen to many people.

Whilst in this hospital I became friendly with various patients, in particular a select handful. One of these patients had a picking compulsion and had picked skin from his body and had had to undergo extensive plastic surgery. Another had the compulsion to walk constantly, despite there being obstacles in front of him. For example, if he was walking in a bus station and there was a brick pillar in his way, he would stop on reaching it, but still carry on the walking movements, not progressing anywhere. I left the Kent hospital and decided to make a go of life and opened my own business – picture-framing. It was successful, but difficult to manage, due to my co-existing conditions, but I somehow struggled on and coped. The next few years saw me struggle from one scenario to another, but even so, during this time I was supported and helped by my parents who must have gone through hell just coping with my odd behaviour, temper tantrums and the like. I just wish there had been more communication between us in the earlier years, which would have eased the burden on us all. But I suppose no one was to blame.

As my life progressed I formed various relationships and a girlfriend lived with me for over three years, but it finally ended due to the pressure of my Tourettes and her insecurities and emotional problems. I live on my own now and have done so for a number of years, and am quite happy. I would never live with someone again unless I felt it was one hundred per cent right. I have dated various girls, but somehow the relationships have never felt quite right for me.

I continued to struggle with my TS, OCD and ADHD, but, compounded by my skin condition, it necessitated spells in hospital for treatment. I travelled thousands of miles to see various doctors and specialists for my skin complaint and was finally diagnosed at St Thomas' Hospital in London – again due to my perseverance to get a name for my condition.

In or around July 1996, my TS took a turn for the worse and I became unable to work and so took some time out, with the help of my parents. But the worst was yet to come. In November 1997, shortly after my girlfriend had left my home after an evening spent with me, I went to bed but found I could not sleep due to a recurring obsessive thought – a destructive compulsion to kill myself. This must not be confused with having suicidal tendencies. Although at times I felt that life wasn't worth living, I did not really contemplate suicide, due to my strong nature. A compulsion can best be described to the average non-suffering person as a thought that enters one's head and the immense anxiety it engenders can only be partially suppressed or controlled. It can be likened to breathing; you can hold your breath for so long, but eventually you have to give in and gasp for air.

I had just developed the compulsion to break my neck. I broke down crying and went to my parents in a state of extreme panic, shock and anxiety and various other fearful emotions which cannot be described on paper. Perhaps they can best be likened to facing a person with a gun, or a knife, who is intent on killing you – only magnified one million times.

I fled to my parents' house. It was now turned 2am. The hospital was called and I went to A & E accompanied by my father, where I was admitted to the psychiatric unit. I stayed for ten days or so. This was most definitely the worst time of my entire life. I could no longer function. The compulsion itself, accompanied by the stress and anxiety of being stopped from doing so, was all consuming. I thought my life had ended. I was heavily sedated and slept for the first two days. On waking, the compulsion was still there, as strong as ever. If I had a compulsion to say, break a cup, I could leave the room where the cup was, but I could not escape from my own body. Unfortunately, I cannot expand and say more about this time in my life as it disturbs and upsets me so much to even think about, let alone write about my feelings.

All this was over two years ago (1997). Now I'm trying to get my life back together. Even so, I continue to struggle hour-by-hour, day-by-day to just get through, it's an uphill struggle but I have to keep trying. I get by and control my odd behaviour and compulsions by saying to myself, "I don't want to do it, so I won't". It doesn't always work, but it helps. I also keep wondering what causes Tourette Syndrome, why such bizarre pointless symptoms, and what have I done to deserve this terrible affliction? Why me?

MY SON'S NOT BAD, HE'S ILL

Michael Bryson's Story by his Mum, Antonia

My story begins on the 19 March 1986, when I gave birth to a beautiful little baby boy, my third child. He weighed nearly nine pounds and had hardly any hair, just little blond spikes. The birth went smoothly apart from the cord being wrapped around his neck and he was whisked away quickly to make sure that he was all right. Everything was fine. He seemed to be very alert and bright, holding up his head and taking in everything around him. This didn't surprise me, since during the last months of my pregnancy he hadn't kept still.

That night the ward was very busy and the nurses were rushed off their feet. I was really tired, as I hadn't had a chance to sleep since my son's birth that morning. He started to cry and nothing would pacify him. After a while, a nurse stopped by and said that she thought he was crying because, although I was breast-feeding him, it could take a day or two for the milk to come through properly, and that I was not to worry. But he cried all night, stopping for only fifteen minutes at a time. No one had time to help, so I cuddled him, walked up and down with him, tried everything I could. Everyone else's babies were quiet, snuggled up asleep in their cribs. In the morning, the lady in the next bed complained about him screaming all night and threw me a dummy that she'd brought in for her own baby, and suggested that I use it. This was the beginning, the first day of his life, and I was to discover that he would upset many more people in the years to follow.

We named him Michael and my husband and I loved him dearly. Things settled down for a while once we were home, until six weeks afterwards when I had to stop breast-feeding because of an infection. He didn't take well to bottled milk and was physically sick a lot. He began to scream through the nights again, and my husband and I had to ask our doctor for help. He then settled down again for a few months. He was such a character – into everything and fascinated by it all. His mind appeared to be way ahead of his co-ordination and this caused him to throw his toys around in frustration. But we would laugh about it, saying he must be the only child who could manage to break Kiddicraft and Fisher-Price toys.

Once Michael was on his feet the baby walker flew around corners on two wheels and our cat left home! He began nursery school at three, but he hated it and would scream and scream. He hated being away from me, although he did eventually settle down – sort of. Later, however, some friends confided that the staff at the nursery were questioning our parenting, because something didn't seem right to them. The nursery staff were reassured by my friends, however, and nothing was said to me directly.

At around the age of four, Michael started grunting and clearing his throat. The doctor thought it was childhood asthma. I mentioned his hyperactivity, since he never seemed to stop and hardly slept. The doctor suggested I cut out coke, cheese, and other things from his diet, but this didn't work, and despite his hyperactivity, Michael could also be very quiet. If he didn't wish to speak, there was no way he would do so, no matter how hard we tried to encourage him. He then began to be obsessed about germs. He wouldn't use other people's toilets and we had to take a potty with us when we went out.

Michael began school at five and, as I heard nothing from the school, I presumed that everything was all right, except that he had trouble using the school toilets and would sometimes not make it home in time, having an accident on the way. He didn't like school and he started to develop twitches, spitting and pulling faces, and he seemed to love anything that was considered to be rude. He would mimic anything and everyone and we swore he would be an actor. We took him to our doctor who told us that the strange things he was doing were called tics and were quite normal, and that Michael was just nervous and would probably outgrow them.

At Michael's first sports day I was shocked by his behaviour. He disrupted everything by pushing the other children out of line. I asked his teacher how long he had been behaving like this, and why hadn't the school told me? I wondered how she coped. Things became worse. Michael had few friends and continued to disrupt classes. His Year 2 teacher thought he was just being naughty when he kept turning his head to one side while she was talking to him, and she poked him in the chest. His tics worsened. He would continually check under his shoes when out walking, he jerked his head, blinked his eyes, shrugged his shoulders, grunted a lot, and spoke swear words aloud, appearing to enjoy the reaction this caused in others. He loved to shock, and needless to say, he wasn't invited to many homes and a lot of parents avoided me.

At the same time he was a sensitive, kind, and thoughtful boy who loved animals and small children. Things became very black and white for him and he was very aware of the injustices of the world. He couldn't understand why people were homeless and starving. "Couldn't they come and live with us? They can have my room," he'd say. He couldn't walk past a beggar without giving him something, even if it was just to share his drink. He would help me get his baby sister's pram through doorways. So why couldn't other people see him as I did? Why did they give him a hard time? Did they not realise the stress they caused him?

school began to call us frequently complaining about Michael's
our. By this time he was being bullied, but his teacher said it was
Michael's fault because he wound everyone up. He ended up in hospital a
few times and was very, very unhappy. He was sleeping very badly and
dreaded going to school, wishing he could break his leg or hurt himself
badly so that he could stay away. Eventually, a school psychologist was
contacted. She concluded that Michael was suffering from depression, but
no medication was offered. She seemed to be more interested in our private
lives and our parenting. I found this very hard to deal with but consoled
myself with the knowledge that our other children were fine.

We co-operated for Michael's sake. We tried good behaviour charts and
ten-minute time out, in which he would be sent to his room if he was
naughty, then we would discuss with him why he had behaved the way he
had. But five minutes later he would do the same thing again, simply
forgetting what had been said earlier. Nothing seemed to work.

Our lives were very busy. My husband and I had started our own
business. We were doing well and employing a few people. I took care of the
paper work and the books which I could do while Michael was at school. But
he was becoming more and more demanding. We dreaded being asked out
as a family because his behaviour was so awful. Life was very stressful, but
looking back, I think we may have been too hard on him. But I couldn't
understand why he behaved so badly. He'd trip people up and yell abuse at
them. At a dance we went to he slid ice cubes across the floor, causing a
young girl to slip and hurt her ankle, and he ran into people like a hurricane.
I approached my doctor about Michael, but I don't think he realised how
difficult the problem was. No help or explanation was offered, and Michael's
tics were still severe although they changed every few months.

In 1995 my marriage broke down and I moved from Scotland down to
England. This was difficult for the children, especially Michael, since he
doesn't cope well with change, good or bad. At his new school his behaviour
created problems all over again. Just to add to my own stress, I found that
people were judging me as an unemployed single parent with no control
over her children.

Then I heard of a lady called Sally Bunday, who runs the Hyperactive
Support Group. I contacted her and was amazed that she could tell me a lot
about Michael without even meeting him. She told me that his behaviour
was typical Attention Deficit Hyperactivity Disorder. I filled in some
questionnaires and answered yes to all the questions. I remember feeling
such relief. It wasn't my fault as a parent. Michael had a chemical imbalance
in his brain. However, this feeling of relief soon changed to anger. Michael
was nine years old, why had nobody realised this before? I explained to
Sally about Michael's tics, that he'd had them since he was four; how they

changed, sometimes being severe, and at other times barely noticeable, and that the longest period he had ever been without them was only twelve weeks. Sally told me of a condition called the Gilles de la Tourette Syndrome. I'd never heard of it, but I filled in more questionnaires, and again answered yes to all the questions. At last I had the answer, and now I had to get a proper diagnosis and some help.

Meantime, Sally had Michael allergy tested and we discovered he had around thirty allergies, including wheat, cheese, full cream milk, food flavourings and colourings. I cut as many of these as I could from his diet. I managed to get gluten-free bread, pasta, and biscuits on prescription, although my food bills increased, which made things very difficult since I was on Income Support. But his behaviour did improve a little, although it was obvious that diet control wasn't enough.

Michael was now seeing a child psychiatrist who didn't happen to know very much about ADHD or Tourette Syndrome. He didn't seem to be very interested in helping Michael either. He was more concerned about the effect Michael's behaviour was having on the rest of my family, and felt that he should go into hospital in order to give us a break, and where he could be observed and diagnosed. This was a difficult decision for me, as I felt that I could cope with Michael. But it was only for twelve weeks, and he would be home at weekends, and a proper diagnosis could be made. So I let him go. I met with the doctor and told him my ideas about diet, which I felt helped Michael. However, he told me that not only would Michael not be kept on the diet – he was not aware of any children being allergic to food – but that he also doubted that Michael was suffering from Tourette Syndrome, since it is very rare.

The next twelve weeks were hell. Michael hated the hospital. He told me he had witnessed children being pinned down by adults and that he was having nightmares. He was locked in the bathroom after getting stressed because no one understood his vocal tic of blowing raspberries on his arm. They thought he was being deliberately disobedient and keeping the other children awake. I spent so much time on the phone, or visiting the hospital, but was told that nothing like that had happened, and that Michael was just causing trouble. I told them that my son did not tell lies and that I believed him. I was not very popular. They claimed he didn't do any tics while they were there, except when he was on the phone to me, so I must make him nervous.

Then they told me that Michael did not have Tourettes. Bad parenting was insinuated and concerns were expressed about his knowledge of sexual matters and words – although apparently he had said nothing to them about this – and that maybe he had been sexually abused in the past. I can't describe how I felt. I had given my consent for them to take my child and they had made things a hundred times worse. I didn't know where to turn. I was sure Michael had never been sexually abused. I was then told that the hospital thought Michael's tics were due to Motor Tic Syndrome, but when I said that that sounded very like Tourettes, they refused to agree, and no medication or treatment was offered.

I had heard of Dr Mary Robinson who was a specialist in TS, and decided to phone her. I spoke to her secretary and poured my heart out – every little detail. I could hardly believe that someone was actually listening to me and taking it all in. Apparently, the waiting list to see Dr Robinson was quite long but her secretary agreed to talk to her for me. I must have sounded very desperate, as I received an appointment in eight weeks' time. By this time, Michael had mentioned suicide several times. He'd tried to choke himself, and was now bullying other kids at school. Things were bad.

When I saw Dr Robinson, she told me that my story was not unique, even down to the suspicion of sexual abuse. Finally, and definitely, Michael was diagnosed with Gilles de la Tourette Syndrome, which included ADHD, OCD, and Coprolalia (compulsive swearing). He also had Oppositional Deficiency Disorder, which was apparently due to lack of understanding. Because of this, he lacked trust in others, and who could blame him, after all he had been through? I don't know why I felt so happy coming home that day. At last, proper answers and explanations, with offers of help and medication. I'm sure it's not right to feel happy that your child has a serious illness, but after everything we'd been through together, it was a relief.

Michael was given Ritalin for his ADHD and Sulpiride for his tics, but finding the right medication was not as simple as I had thought. He didn't react well to the Sulpiride, it made him hyper, and I couldn't increase the Ritalin, because that made his tics worse. He attacked three teachers at school and he was expelled. This meant that he had to be tutored at home for a year, while attempts were made to have him statemented. Medication is still being tried and tested with him now and we are three years on. Some of them work for a while, and things had improved immensely until he was sent back to school. Unfortunately, he was sent to a school for children with emotional and behavioural difficulties, because it was felt by the authorities that he needed to be placed in that category, but Michael is very bright and does not need help with learning.

Even with a diagnosis, life is hard. People don't understand TS. Teachers don't know enough about it, so the way they deal with it only makes things more difficult, and other children make fun of the tics. Meanwhile, Michael is struggling hard. For me, trying to make people aware of this disorder, finding the right school and medication, and trying to bring a little happiness into Michael's life is all I can do. But I don't know what the future holds.

The worst thing has been to hear that Michael, "has to fit into society". What has happened to the individual? We're all different, with different characteristics, disabilities and illnesses. Why can't we be more understanding, accepting of people, and caring? Michael is right. There are many injustices in this world. Only you and I can change them.

I HATE HAVING TOURETTES

Michael Bryson, aged twelve

My tics stop me watching television, and playing football, I have to bang my teeth together, flick the floor with my hand, check all the electrical switches are off, I move my head and touch things with my nose.

I have to take tablets like Ritalin, Prozac, Clonidine, Pimozide, Imipramine and Dexedrine that don't work. People take the piss and call me names like 'Bangy Teeth' and 'Nosey'. My teachers don't understand. They send me out of the classroom, tell me off and hold my head to stop me moving. When I was younger, a teacher said I was doing it on purpose and poked me in the chest. I've had nightmares and I imagine things that are not there, and I don't like being on my own.

Everybody thinks that I annoy them on purpose, like when I have to keep tying my shoelaces all the time. I get stressed all the time and I break my favourite things. I've cut off my hair before, pulled out my teeth, cut my eyebrows and eyelashes. I need to get baths or showers a lot and I need my clothes to smell clean.

HELP!

Richard Buston

As a war baby, I was born the second son of a vicar at Cumnor Vicarage, just outside Oxford. A few years into my life, at the age of four, I began compulsively picking at a hole in the plaster on the wall above my bedroom window. It became extremely exasperating to me, as the hole got ever larger.

At the age of five, I could not leave my bedroom door without rubbing my fingers on the door handle, and saying, several times over, the numbers three and four until I had got it 'right' and was happy enough to leave it. Even so, I sometimes rushed back for just one more.

At the age of six, I began, dangerously, to lift the front wheel of my tricycle in traffic. I particularly remember the face of the driver of a red double-decker bus, as I continuously did one of my tricycle obsessions in front of his bearing down bus. At that time I was at a local school, and one day, when I couldn't resist picking all the sticky buds off a shrub in the headmaster's garden, I only just missed a thrashing. I also topped dozens of tulip heads in my parents' garden at the vicarage, and these incidents now tell me that I already had the potential to develop TS.

In 1949, I was sent off to boarding school in Sussex, at the age of eight. My symptoms had left me and I was top of the class in nearly everything for over a year and the future looked good. However, in January 1951 I contracted flu when living at Ascot Rectory, and later, in February, I found myself unable to do my work properly and was beaten for it by the headmaster. This was probably due to ADD, and at the same time, I was making noises and sucking in air. As I worsened, I was placed in the school sanatorium, where I spent the rest of the term.

In the following school holidays, I became very disturbed, making even more persistent vocal tics. Nobody knew what was wrong. Our GP thought it might be Chorea (St Vitus' Dance – a nervous disease causing irregular involuntary movements of the limbs and face) and sent me to Taplow Red Cross Memorial Hospital near Maidenhead for six weeks. During this time no other diagnosis was made.

In July of 1951 I returned home well rested, with symptoms gone for the time being. But they soon returned, with a vengeance, and my parents hired a twenty-four hour nurse to look after me. By this time I was having some really bad tantrums and started emptying bookcases down the stairs in tremendous rages. Stones from the garden were thrown through the large rectory windows. I was in a right state. We went to the races to watch

Supreme Court win the Festival Stakes (now King George VI & Queen Elizabeth Stakes), and I tore up my race card and embarrassed my mother and her friends by lying on my back and venting a tremendous rage. Later, I was to leave these rages behind me. After moving to Enfield in Middlesex, I returned to Ascot for an autumn race meeting where I couldn't stop shouting obscenities in the paddock. It certainly gave the bookies in the paddock in front of the stands something to laugh about!

At the end of July of that year, my parents took me to Harley Street, where various psychologists were interested only in whether I had been involved in homosexual acts at boarding school. Freud was king! I also saw the eminent neurologist of the day, Sir Russell Braine, who also could only concentrate on the boarding school homosexual angle, probably because I was punctuating my sentences at diagnosis.

Eventually, during that summer, a well-known child psychiatrist, Dr Kenneth Cameron, said I must have developed encephalitis (brain inflammation) as a result of the flu I had had six months previously. It seems more likely now that I was showing the signs of full blown Tourette Syndrome. Dr Cameron admitted me to his children's ward at the Maudsley Hospital in London. I cried for two weeks because I thought a dirty trick had been played on me. I remember that, after I had been there a month, a male night nurse came into the dormitory and grabbed me as I lay in bed, saying, "Did you make that noise? Well shut up, then." He then took another boy out of his bed and into the bathroom where he abused him. The rest of the staff were very good, I am relieved to say. There were other very disturbed children there, with what now seems to me to have been TS, and also some epileptics. It was a dreadful environment for a nine-year-old, and I had begun to develop Echolalia (repetition of words).

In 1952 my symptoms waned and I was allowed to leave the Maudsley. I was sent to Papplewick Boys School at Ascot, where I became very good at swimming and diving.

In September of 1952 I returned to Newlands School at Seaford in Sussex, where I started kneeling in the playground with my hands clasped, saying, "Oh, my God!" The other boys named me 'Barmy Buston', but I gradually settled down and had few TS problems, due, no doubt, to being sedated with Phenobarbitone. I had a good period up to taking my common entrance exams for Bryanston School in Dorset in the summer of 1955, when I averaged a sixty-six per cent rate, with one hundred per cent in the arithmetic paper. Tourettes must have been in abeyance then.

At Bryanston I allowed myself to become the naughtiest boy in my year, and, as yet, Tourettes was still not rearing its ugly head. However, in the spring of 1956, I resolved to be good so that I would be promoted to a senior house, but the strain began to take its toll in the summer term at senior house level. The homosexuality there was disturbing, and my Attention Deficit Disorder (ADD) returned in force. I was no longer able to work properly, Tourettes was coming back, and I was starting to break down.

In the summer holidays of that year, Tourettes returned with a vengeance. I remember most the compulsive handstands in the street, and worrying about kicking people in the teeth in Piccadilly Circus! I was very unsure of myself – a complete mess, and very depressed – so I hid away in my bedroom at Enfield Vicarage most of the time. In the autumn of that year, Dr Cameron admitted me to his adolescents' ward, Tyson East Two, at Bethlem Royal Hospital. There were some very disturbed children there and Tourettes was rife. If I were not already Touretting, I soon would be. There was a boy ripping up his own and other people's clothing, and another would alternately pick at his eyes and genitals. Some had movement obsessions and others had walking obsessions. What a hellhole! There were a lot of very aggressive boys there, too, as well as manic-depressives. All in all, my education was swiftly being put into reverse gear.

It wasn't long before I was clapping my hands over my ears and shouting, "menstruation", much to the amusement of some of the hospital staff. I thought the boy who was compelled to repeat, "I love you, Dr Cameron", making Dr Cameron angry, was very amusing (in a nice sort of way), but the doctor didn't think so. I called him "Cammy" but he never knew that. He never said anything to me except that I didn't have to repeat obscenities. He couldn't have known about TS, or simply just did not accept it. He preferred to pop me with hormone pills and then LSD treatment, which never did me any good. How could it? My mind was okay. I just had a neurologically-disordered brain.

After a break, in 1958, I was back in Bethlem in 1959 and 1960. Intolerance and teasing was often the order of the day, because a 'Touretter' is so disturbing to other patients, especially when shouting, "Help!" at night when others were trying to sleep, as in my case. I couldn't blame them, though, so I simply stuck a sheet in my mouth. I still stuff handkerchiefs in my mouth at night so as not to disturb my family. Even staff would call out "Help" to imitate me, or even worse, use it to call me. Many people are cruel to Touretters, and I really began to use that particular word when I encountered a policeman whilst on holiday in 1957.

I had a Welsh girlfriend in Bethlem, but it was a difficult relationship because she thought a lot of things were contaminated and this made love-making a problem a times. A farm worker had abused her as a child and she had a serious hand-washing obsession. The woods around Bethlem were a romantic's paradise, although, as a Touretter, one had to be careful not to give the game away. Suppressing the "helps!" was necessary to avoid being spotted.

While at Bethlem I saw others having electric current and insulin treatment, and I was very relieved that I was not subjected to such horrors. After I left in January 1961, they put my girlfriend to sleep for three months. I never found out whether it did her any good. The psychiatrist, Dr Cameron, died in 1962 without ever mentioning TS to my family or me.

In 1961, my first ever job was in a kennels in Hampshire. I lasted four days, living in. The owner could not accept the 'vocals'. But in that year I learned to drive. This was a good achievement for me, especially as my symptoms were waning once more. In the summer I got a job as an assistant cowman on a dairy farm in Bedfordshire. Unfortunately, I started shouting "Help!" again, much to the annoyance of the head cowman. I lasted six months. Tourettes had won again.

In 1962 I worked at Rochford's pot plant nursery, in Hertfordshire. My symptoms weren't too bad that year, and, feeling better, I bought a horse to have at livery near Potters Bar, where I met my first wife. I was doing well and Tourettes was doing well. I stayed at Rochford's for a year or so, then got married by my father at Enfield Church and went to live with my wife near Chichester, where I got a job in a chrysanthemum nursery. A year later, my first daughter was born. However, my wife and I weren't very compatible and I became agitated again, breaking windows in our cottage and at the nursery. Vocal tics started to appear as well, and I had to leave the nursery, as the strain was getting horrendous.

It was now 1964 and I managed to get some work on a nearby farm. All these jobs I had been forced to take over the years were because of TS. I had no chance of reaching higher and developing my potential – Tourettes made sure of that!

In 1965 it was time to move, and for the price of my Elizabethan cottage in Sussex, I was able to buy a small farm in Devon, where our two sons were born. But the vocals started up again and the "helps!" thundered across the valley where the farm stretched. However, I was fortunate enough to have some investment income, otherwise our married life would have been impossible.

During the period from 1967 to 1970 I had studied and passed GCE, O and A Level subjects and started on a teacher training course at St Luke's College in Exeter, but I just could not face trying to be a teacher – not after the experience of teaching practice. Tourettes saw that off, too.

In 1971 we moved farms and started breeding Arab horses on the edge of Dartmoor. Then in 1972 my wife ran off with a hippy. Strangely, this caused my symptoms to ease off for a while. I had several driving jobs – and a few relationships to distract me, too. I worked as a laundryman, a milkman, a frozen food driver/salesman, and a yeast driver/salesman. But in the last of these, the obsessional side of TS started to get worse. I was pushing my denture down my throat and jumping on my heels with a rigid body. Also obscenities again came to the fore (though quietly when women were present), and my head jerking became more frequent.

In 1977, I divorced my first wife, and in 1978 I married my present wife, Sally. We have two daughters aged fourteen and twelve. Sally has been so good to me. I can't blame her for getting angry and unhappy with the syndrome in the past (especially the vocals which can get very pornographic), because we didn't know about Tourettes at all until March 1994. Now that she knows what the problem is, however, it is much easier for her to cope. But going back to 1992, I got my denture stuck down my throat and it went too far and had to be extracted under a general anaesthetic in Torbay Hospital. Then, last Christmas, I swallowed a teaspoon. It came out after a month of pain.

My wife is now at home with me all the time to avoid such occurrences happening again, but the obscenities and shouting keep on coming – please wane soon! I hate drugs because they just knock me down. I am trying hard to get myself into a state of relaxation and non-concern that will maybe lessen the need to vocalise and jerk about.

All of my five children are fit and happy, though one or two could be carriers of the TS gene. I worry about their children in the future. I already have a granddaughter of eighteen months.

I have not yet mentioned the many obsessions I have in the home. Along with compulsive swallowing of inedible objects, I have had obsessional arranging, using numbers, ie counting how many times I do certain things, and bashing windows, always hoping that they won't break. Also, I have obsessions with my teeth, pulling or grinding them, though I don't risk wearing a four-toothed plate any more. Eye poking, pulling my jaw downwards, how many more are there? But a lot of them ease when stress eases.

I am fifty-two now but I shan't be working again. Maybe voluntary work one day. I have been wise financially, investing instead of spending my money, so my dividends pay my bills now and, hopefully, in the future – wars both military and trade permitting! I can still drive, though I don't enjoy it much, but my accident record is excellent. Only two claims on my policy in thirty-three years of driving.

Fortunately, I don't have any near neighbours, except for the people who have stables and horses in a field across the road. They laugh at me, of course. Should I laugh with them? Or should I cry? Perhaps I should just stick the old hankie in and retreat to the house when they are around. Hell knows! I commiserate with and love all Touretters. You deserve all the understanding you can find.

I BELIEVE I CAN FLY

Hollie Crabtree's Story by her Mum, Carole

Let me introduce my family to you. My name is Carole and I am a play specialist. My husband Ian works as a surveyor, and we are both hard-working, sociable people. Our eldest son, Andrew, is eighteen years old, and is a friendly, lively lad. David is our second born and he is thirteen years old. He is quiet, sensitive, and academic. Our family is complete with our beautiful ten-year-old daughter, Hollie. On the surface, we are a 'normal' family unit, or so it would appear to the outside world, except that the behaviour of our daughter belies the happy unit exterior. We are not a normal family. We do not live a normal family life, and never will do. For, to differing degrees, we all grieve.

Our daughter first gave us cause for concern when she was still in her cot. She began to display signs of obsessive compulsive behaviour, although at the time we were unaware of its clinical existence. In her cot she would not, or perhaps, could not sleep without her blankets covering her in the correct order. Eventually, I realised this, and life became easier. Instinctively, Ian and I learned of her increasing obsessions by trial and error. Her bottle milk had to be heated to exactly the correct temperature. The feeder cup had to be exactly central. When she started feeding herself, she would use the spoons only once, and would go through many spoons before completing her meal. I would have to line all our spoons alongside her dish. My work colleagues suggested I was spoiling her, and that she was doing these things just for attention. I did not think this was the case, but began to doubt my parenting skills. Could it be that by acknowledging her obsessions, I was, in fact, feeding them? Was I helping them to develop? The answer to this still plagues me, and I wonder if I will ever find the answer.

As she has grown older, her OCD has been a driving force in our family, for it affects *all* the family, not just Hollie and me. Being her mother, and knowing her so well, I accept her behaviour, adapting my own life in order to make Hollie's daily life easier. For example, she still has difficulties with sleeping with the bedclothes in particular ways, and although the obsessions vary as to how the covers should be, I interpret her need and make her bed exactly how she wants it to be. She still checks her bed every night before settling down, but she is reassured in knowing that it is initially correct, and this prevents overt distress from the onset. Unfortunately, I am the only one who seems to have this affinity with her needs, which is a great trial, and places a daily burden on my shoulders.

Hollie's OCD is constant and never wanes. She is obsessed about her bed, her clothing, particularly socks, and the fit of her shoes varies from being so slack they slip off her feet, to being so tight that they nip and bruise her skin. Her compulsions include touching hot objects, putting her fingers in closing doors, touching and sniffing things, evening things up, checking everything, repeating songs and phrases endlessly (Palilalia), obsessive thoughts which are at times sexual, and very often she is haunted by fearsome mental images. At one time she was the only child going to school in a coat with a hood on it to prevent her from looking at the sun. In the middle of summer!

Her most severe obsessions are food fads, and at the moment she is compulsively eating until she is close to vomiting and her weight is ballooning. Our way of coping with her behaviour is to pre-empt the situations as far as possible, to adjust our lives accordingly, and wait patiently without fuss or comment, until the compulsive/obsessive act is completed.

I do not wish to sound like the perfect mother, for I am not. For many years I experienced times of great frustration and anger. In the past, my anger towards my daughter's behaviour could be tremendous and all consuming, to a point I had never known before. I have had to shout, scream at her, grit my teeth, and walk away many times. But now that I have accepted her OCD as a dimension of her character, my anger has lessened, my patience is greater, and I can usually manage to be accepting and calm.

I firmly believe that acceptance of your child's behaviour helps by constantly remembering that it is not intended to be purposeful or malicious, nor is it intended to drive you wild. Terrible though it all is for the parents, for the child it must be totally harrowing. So thinking, at difficult times, not of yourself, but of your child, helps you to focus. There are times when I do feel self-pity for my trials but it is never expressed in front of my daughter. It is kept for the arms of my husband.

To describe Tourette Syndrome to anyone who is unaware of it, tics would be a major component. Although Hollie's OCD is her life, we have adapted to her, gradually, daily. However, it was because of her ticcing that we sought help.

The ticcing started with eye twitching and facial grimaces. When she was six years old she was given the privilege of playing the part of Mary in the school nativity play. We instructed her to sit on her hands throughout. This she did, but her face twitched constantly. Our hearts were filled with an intense love, compassion, and protection, for our beautiful daughter. But we also experienced embarrassment, unease, and maybe, fear. As it happened, we had nothing to fear, because only our eyes saw our daughter's twitching become more pronounced as her anxiety increased. Everyone else was concentrating on their own child.

By the age of seven, Hollie began having vocal tics. Sniffing can easily be overlooked in any child, but when grunting became severe, we really did need help. The grunting began to dissolve our daily family life. She could not stop the noise in the evening when her tiredness exacerbates all her behaviour. We would sit down as a complete family to watch an hour of television before going to bed. When the grunting began, one by one her brothers would become irritated by the constant noise and would leave and go to bed early. Eventually, Ian would go, too, and I would be left alone with her. I am totally ashamed to admit it, but sometimes I would also leave Hollie to watch television alone. I feel guilt as well as shame for my own actions.

We could no longer go to church, the cinema, or even on public transport, because people would turn around and look at her. So we took her to our GP. Fortunately, our GP is competent and he immediately referred her to a child psychologist. Within two weeks she had been diagnosed as having Gilles de la Tourette Syndrome. We were relieved, saddened, and frightened. Our old values, life, and family, passed on, and I use the words 'passed on' deliberately. Because for the first twelve months we experienced a grieving period. We grieved for our life as normal parents and family. We grieved for the life that would never be, and ultimately, we grieved for the life that Hollie will never have. A new path had been born.

Hollie was put on the drug, Haloperidol, two years ago. The tics, including eye rolling, mouth stretching, and any combination of grimaces, are always changing. As a new one appears, so another abates and disappears until its turn to re-emerge again. But now the intensity and aggressiveness has diminished, they are less noticeable and less pronounced. Social and peer interaction is again an option. Grunting has become minimal, and in order to help, we make sure that we sit apart from others if possible, on buses, at the cinema, or in public places. School assembly is difficult. Initially, Hollie would go to the end of the line so that she could move without disturbing the other children. But the grunting, more audible in the quiet of prayer time, encourages the other children to laugh at her, and some mimic her. The problem for the teachers is that, in not reprimanding Hollie, (for they are fully aware of her condition and understand it), they do need to reprimand those children who are mimicking her. But which grunt is Hollie's? When her tics are intense, Hollie now waits in her classroom until assembly is over. But sad exclusion and isolation compound her feelings of low self-esteem. From other sufferers we have spoken to, we have discovered that Haloperidol causes dullness of the mind. Being her parents we are aware of this, but some advocates for Hollie debate the medication. Hollie has always been a demanding and restless child. Sitting still presents problems.

She spends the day twirling, performing handstands, cartwheels, chatting, singing, and displaying general clumsiness as she rushes at everything. Having a cuddle has always been fraught with irritation and constant changing of position. Verbal communication is also constant, even in sleep, for she appears to be unable to rest. She walks, talks, and even does handstands in her sleep. Although Hollie has not been specifically diagnosed as having ADHD, we do believe there is an element of it in her behaviour. She suffers from poor impulse control, quickly loses her temper, and throws objects. We have had five internal doors broken, and our intact possessions are slowly dwindling. Her group of loyal friends mainly accept this aspect of her behaviour, but if I feel she is being too demanding or physical, I bring her inside, or send the girls home. When she is playing, I monitor the situation occasionally and assess her level by her verbal conversations.

A more private aspect of Hollie's behaviour has been her self-harming. Through years of constantly trying to be 'normal', hiding her behaviour problems, and waiting to grow out of it all, Hollie has developed a very low self-esteem. She feels incomplete, struggling, a hopeless person. This has manifested itself in various forms of self-harming. Hair pulling, head banging, chest thumping, face gouging. Anything to cause herself pain. She says that the more painful it is, the better she feels. We have tried several forms of restriction, physical (pinning down), time out alone in a room, a punch bag, but all to no avail. The desire to inflict pain on herself is too great.

The only release appears to be when she can punch me. It began with the occasional punch or slap, and developed into several powerful intense attacks when her impulse was at its peak. I accepted this with some bewilderment, wondering if she felt the need to punish me for what she was going through. After the outbursts of aggression had subsided, we could talk easily together, and she has always maintained that punishment is not the case. She would, however, cry endlessly, repeatedly apologising. She feels such deep remorse for her actions that it makes my heart weep for my little girl, that she should have to experience such profound emotions daily. But because the abuse and aggression was increasing to sometimes twice daily episodes, it was gaining in momentum and power. I never feel any anger now towards my daughter, and never retaliate in any way except to try to restrain her. I am filled with a sense of compassion and pain for her, because I know that when she is tired and her aggression has passed, her guilt is becoming too much for her to bear. But I am her mother, her rock, and if I cannot accept her Tourettes in its entirety, if I cannot love her absolutely without condition, then how can she ever accept herself, and learn to love herself, as she needs to?

One Saturday evening, she tried to commit suicide. Her vision of dying, as a ten-year-old, is being run over by a vehicle. This is precisely what she tried to do. She undid her seat-belt in the car while we were travelling on a busy road, and tried to open the door and jump out. I scrambled to get her back in. Our depths of despair had reached rock bottom. An emergency meeting was arranged with her doctor who spoke at length with Hollie. He also spoke to both our sons in private at their request. He then arranged for myself and Ian to attend advanced parenting skills sessions. These sessions have been helpful for us. We discuss individual situations and take advice about our reactions. The key statement has been to always be positive about Hollie's actions, feelings and fears, and in particular, about her future. Her aggression has decreased to an acceptable level, but whether that is in response to the skills sessions, or to the natural waxing and waning of the symptoms, we will never know. To help her, we have tried aromatherapy massage sessions with a professional psychotherapist, and for some hours afterwards she is relaxed and the experience appears to be successful. She is free from tension and the tics are minimal. But these effects are short-lived and the following day she is back to her normal self.

Hollie has recently been attending clinics with an occupational therapist at the request of her psychologist. She has had six to date and they are held in strict confidence. Hollie admits that they help her to vocalise and acknowledge her deep-set fears and provide an outlet to explore them. She wishes to continue the sessions.

Living with a child with TS is a constant roller coaster of emotions. During a single day we can experience intense love, pride and protection, through to anger, frustration, guilt and despair. As her parents, these daily yo-yos impede our own self-esteem, and depression creeps around the periphery of our existence. Life is a constant battle for us, too, and some of this filters through to our extended family. Grandparents, aunts, and uncles, run the gauntlet to a lesser degree. My friends are constantly concerned for our welfare. This has led to one dear friend giving us the gift of respite care by having Hollie stay overnight, and is taking her on holiday soon. I have already bought tickets to take David to Alton Towers. Ian and I try hard not to neglect our sons.

Saturday has become our day off. This is because while we were trying to find Hollie an activity that would suit her, we stumbled across a smallholding advertising a pets club. This has developed successfully and Hollie currently stables a horse there. She now spends all day Saturday grooming Sari, her horse, but that is all. Any more time than that and she would get too tired, so the horse is loaned out to other children on other days. She loves her time at the smallholding and comes home feeling relaxed and happy. Animals have become her passion. This gives Ian and myself time to take out Ian's father from his nursing home for a couple of hours. He has been there for two years because of Alzheimer's disease.

Hollie is a very sociable, friendly, and compassionate child. Sometimes we glimpse her real personality when the Tourettes is not too strong. She is loving and considerate and has a good sense of humour. Her perceptions of herself and her life are remarkable. She often dreams that she is trying to fly but can never leave the ground. She interprets this to mean that she is trying to overcome her problems and is never quite managing it. Her theme tune recently has been *I Believe I can Fly*, by R Kelly. She often sings this when she is feeling low, and is determined one day to fly in her dreams. When she does, I will know that she has found some measure of peace with herself.

Our life with our daughter has been difficult, but we have good times, too. Acquaintances often say how lucky she is to have us for her family, but it is we who are the lucky ones, for she has made our family complete with her exuberance, her love, and her dynamic personality.

And, finally, a note from my beautiful daughter herself ...

MY LIFE WITH TOURETTES

Hollie Crabtree, aged ten

Hi, my name is Hollie. My mum might have already told you a lot about my life and how I cope with it, but this is from my point of view.

When I first started school, I was made fun of. People would ask me, "Why do you do these things?" I would answer, for example, if I sniff (like I think a lot of you would, if you had Tourettes), I would make up I had a cold as an excuse. Now I am older though, I tell them to f... off. When I started my new school in class four I met a friend and I told her all about my syndrome and how I handle my life. She understands and tells me to persevere and tries to help me at school.

When I come home from school I am really tired. I go to bed at about 6.30pm. I can't play out with my friends, because when I'm tired, I feel like a volcano. Say if we went out for the day, we can't stay very long, or go very far, because I am tired. Even shopping for clothes is a nightmare. I am okay in the mornings, but I can get really aggressive.

My temper is the worst. I'm always frustrated in my mind. I can't think straight. I don't know what to say; I just want to swear. I EXPLODE completely.

RIGHT OUT OF THE BLUE

Hayley Gould's Story by her Mum, Karen

Having lived with this condition for eight years, and seeing it manifest itself in two of our children, the following is an account of the problems and mistakes we have encountered in learning to live with Tourette Syndrome and its associated disorders.

Our daughter, Hayley, was born on 12 November 1984. The birth was fine with no complications. Hayley is our second child. She sailed through all her developmental milestones, and everything seemed fine. But things began to change as she approached two. If she fell over, or hurt herself, she would cry, but without tears, her eyes would roll into the back of her head and she would go limp. Although it was all over in a matter of seconds, it was, nevertheless, a frightening experience and it caused a lot of problems for our family. Hayley being our second child did not make things any easier for us as parents. We were young and not very confident, and still learning different things about parenthood; trying to keep up with the pressures of what society expects, what was right or wrong, what should, or should not, be given to our children.

Family life became increasingly difficult because of Hayley's blackout problems, causing tension between my husband and myself. Each of us took the attitude, "Well, it's your family. You deal with it." Our other daughter, Stacey, if asked to play with Hayley, would simply bust into tears. She seemed frightened, which shocked us. We decided to see our GP and ask for a referral to investigate this problem, in case it was something important.

In August 1986, we received an appointment to see a paediatrician. Things were getting more difficult at home, as Hayley had begun to display aggressive behaviour and was throwing herself down on the floor with intent to hurt herself. The doctor's advice was to ignore the behaviour and pay her no attention. But we felt this was dangerous, and not good advice. Being closely involved, as Hayley's mother, I burst into tears with the appalling feeling of, "They don't know what it is like at home". The doctor agreed to keep Hayley in hospital for a weekend so my husband and I could have a break. When Hayley came home we were advised to ignore the behaviour. We were left feeling distressed and more worried than before. It makes one uneasy when no explanations are offered, because the human mind works on reassurance.

Our daughter was three years old, and about to start a new chapter in her life by going to playgroup and becoming independent. Problems began within the first two weeks. Hayley hated the separation, or maybe just leaving home, who knows? She entered playgroup in tears, kicking and screaming, sometimes starting before she left the car, and had to be carried out. After many months of this, we could see it was harming her emotionally, so we stopped taking her. Instead, I started taking her to a mother and toddler group, knowing how important it was for both of us to be involved socially with other children and their parents. Since I could stay with Hayley it would satisfy both our needs. Hayley seemed happy, so it seemed the right time to move her on to a nursery, since she was now almost four.

She settled down there, much to our relief, and we began to relax. Then she began to flick her head as if she was flicking her hair out of her eyes. This went on for some months until the teacher asked us if we knew why she kept on doing it. We took her to the doctor because, by this time, we had noticed persistent throat clearing and sniffing. He told us that her head movements would stop, she would grow out of them, and eventually we thought he must be right because they gradually eased off. But she was given antibiotics on three occasions for her constant throat clearing and sniffing.

After many visits to our GP and the paediatrician, we began to feel that we were considered to be neurotic and over-protective parents. We felt we were not being taken seriously, and began to wonder if there was something different about our daughter. Breath-holding attacks were still happening and each time they seem harder to deal with, especially as she was wetting herself during them. We went back to our doctor and emphasised how worried and stressed we were, and he organised a brain scan. However, the scan revealed nothing and again we were told that she would grow out of it.

In 1990 Hayley started primary school, and for a while there were no problems. At her school medical, on explaining about Hayley's history, we were told to stop comparing her with our other daughter, Stacey.

In 1990 our son, Nicholas, was born. A healthy eight-pound boy, and again, no birth complications. He was accepted by both girls with open arms, but like Hayley, he did nothing but cry. We seemed to be unable to calm him, no matter what we tried. We were still worried about Hayley, as she now seemed to be suffering emotional problems. She found mixing and making friends hard work, and tended to play by herself more and more, jumping about, singing, shouting and twirling. But it all happened in our garden, out of sight of everybody but me.

Junior school became a real problem when she began to run out, and in 1993, when a teacher was reprimanding another child, she saw that Hayley was laughing at her. So Hayley was ordered out into the playground and made to stand in a torrential thunderstorm without even her coat. Hayley waited for a while, then she ran home. How she got out of the school grounds and was not hurt crossing a busy main road, I will never know. It took a considerable amount of effort to calm her down and we called the school and asked for an explanation. The head was extremely unsupportive and unsympathetic about the whole incident. We explained that Hayley was worried about upsetting her teacher again and didn't want to return, so it was suggested that we try another school further away, that perhaps a bus journey would provide the answer. We were very upset that nobody would take responsibility for what had happened. We had understood that children were safe when in school. But how safe? was our question.

The Local Education Authority was unable to find a suitable school for Hayley, and we were dissatisfied about the situation since she was missing a lot as the weeks slipped by. We decided to appeal to a local school, but we received a visit from an education welfare officer about what we intended to do. This made matters worse, increasing the pressure and stress that we were already under. It did not seem like a good idea to force Hayley back to the school she had run away from, but there was a lot of disagreement between us and the LEA as to what was in Hayley's best interests, and what we felt was best for her. We found ourselves under such pressure that we agreed to send her to a Catholic school for a while, at least until the appeal we had lodged for the local school was heard. We wanted Hayley back at school as quickly as possible, but were also trying to save her further stress.

In March 1993 we found out that we had lost the appeal for the local junior school. On studying the appeal information, we discovered a discrepancy in their findings about the intake of pupils, a difference between the figures quoted by the school and the figures presented at the appeal. We contacted the LEA and told them we intended to take legal advice, but a few days later we had a letter stating that they had changed their minds. This was a tremendous relief, knowing that Hayley was close to home if she should have any difficulties or problems at school, and she settled in fine, despite her horrendous past. However, it was not long before she started eye blinking, and complained that her vision was "blurry". We took her to an optician, but an eye test revealed nothing wrong. Then her teacher asked to see us regarding problems between Hayley and four other girls, saying that she thought Hayley was, "too sensitive".

We decided at this time to move house, and found a suitable property with a local nursery and playgroup as well as a school for Hayley. Nicholas, now three, was ready for playgroup, but he, too, had problems settling in. I couldn't help feeling that we'd been down this road before, but we had to persevere. After all, as the staff kept reminding us, all children dislike parting from their mothers. Hayley hadn't minded changing her school, but felt that she was being made fun of, and we were almost afraid that she was becoming paranoid. Meanwhile, Nicholas had started eye blinking and his eyes kept watering. Our GP thought it might be hay fever because his eyes were red and bloodshot. However, he gave him nothing for the condition.

Hayley's school reports were due and we were very worried. She had started making yelping noises, like a puppy. We didn't know what to make of it, but hoped it would soon stop and thought perhaps she was copying something, or somebody, from school. But her report was awful. Her teacher complained about the untidiness of her writing, careless mistakes, and the distraction her yelps and giggles caused in class. Hayley, however, complained about being made to stand with her nose against the wall, as punishment. We decided to take the matter to our GP again, but he felt it was nothing to worry about. It was probably 'middle child syndrome'! We had never heard of this and asked if there was some way of treating it, and he referred Hayley to a child and family unit for children with behavioural and emotional problems.

The appointment for this arrived in August 1995, and we had coped alone for a month, not knowing what was wrong. We were finding it hard to deal with Hayley. We began to punish her a lot, sending her to her bedroom, stopping her doing things she wanted to do, and shouting at her. We even tried to bribe her, but nothing worked. She was now jerking her head and grunting as well as yelping. As her mother, I felt totally helpless. It was as though whatever was wrong with her, it was now looming over our heads and getting out of control. We often asked her why she did such things, but the answer was always, "I don't know", except that on one occasion she said that she, "caught her problems from a friend at school".

The consultant at the child and family unit asked if we had heard of Tourette Syndrome, and we had, but only from a television programme. They did not enlighten us and we were too shocked to ask. We soon realised that we were not getting any help from anyone, so decided that we would have to do it ourselves, and went to the library and looked up Tourette Syndrome. What we found was that Hayley was exhibiting classic symptoms, but the child and family unit did not seem inclined to discuss anything with us. We felt that nothing was being done. Hayley resented having to leave school for her appointments during class time, and we began to wonder if she was being used as a guinea pig.

We approached our GP again in the hope that he could arrange for us to see someone who would understand these problems, because by now Nicholas was clinging to me in the same way Hayley had – kicking, screaming and punching me when I tried to leave him at the playgroup. I gave in, thinking it was not worth all the stress and anxiety. But Hayley was admitted to a London hospital ward for tests and a brain scan, which, unfortunately, revealed nothing. The doctors seemed to be at a loss, until we showed them a ten-minute video we had made of Hayley at home, and it was then confirmed that she did have Tourette Syndrome. We were told that she would need her GP's referral to attend a TS clinic and that she would need to be statemented. We went home feeling cheated. We wanted to know more than anything why Hayley was being denied her childhood – and how we would cope.

Again we ended up with no answers, but informed the school of the diagnosis and contacted the educational psychologist to discuss statementing. Thankfully, our son seemed to be looking forward to starting nursery school and we were hoping he would settle down. After seven weeks with the child and family unit, we still felt that we were not learning anything that would help; no strategies, no therapy, and Hayley was getting worse. Mealtimes were difficult, she was getting very aggressive, and her grunting was making it impossible for us to take her out, because passers-by thought we were mistreating her. So we asked our GP for a referral to the TS clinic, since we felt that the child and family unit did not appear to be meeting Hayley's needs. Later we discovered that the unit was, in fact, concentrating on the effect we, as a family, were having on her. They didn't seem to understand that she had a neurological problem.

We felt very guilty, and ignorant, for not realising that Hayley's problems were not her fault, and that we had let her down as parents for punishing her as we did and not loving her enough. We had made a terrible mistake, but now we had to come to terms with that and look to the future. While we waited for her appointment for the TS clinic, our doctor put her on Clonidine. However, this seemed to make her more restless, more argumentative, and generally noisier, but we decided to keep with it in the meantime.

Hayley attended the TS clinic in November 1995 and was assessed for treatment. It was agreed that she did have Tourette Syndrome, but that her behaviour problems were caused by something else. This left us even more confused, if that was possible, especially as it was not made clear what this 'something else' could be. It was suggested that she take Pimozide for her tics, and that we should take her back in three month's time. But even though Hayley now had her diagnosis, it didn't seem to make any difference to her at school. She was still being accused of being over-sensitive, too demanding, and always seeking attention and was often told to suppress her tics and noises because of the other children, despite being laughed at and teased by them. She felt deeply hurt. We had done our best to explain her condition to the school, that it was involuntary, and that suppressing it would cause her more anxiety and stress, and made it clear that we felt that we were not being taken seriously and that Hayley was in danger of becoming a victim of a system, which was supposed to be helping her.

We decided then to join the Tourette Syndrome (UK) Association, who we thought would help us to support and care for Hayley. We were being told by our well-meaning family members and by teachers that Hayley was normal, but we could see that she was suffering psychological problems and emotional pain, and she, herself, was afraid that she would die because of it. We felt numb. Nicholas was having difficulties at nursery and was refusing to go, but the staff told us not to give in and, of course, we had been through all this before. We decided to have him allergy tested, but our doctor refused to do it, so we had to go to a private clinic. When the results arrived, we discovered that he was allergic to sugar, milk and E numbers. We put him on a special diet, but it didn't improve his behaviour and it was proving even more difficult to get him to nursery. We asked the staff for help, to interact with him as soon as he arrived in order to distract him, and they were very sympathetic and helpful. The results were encouraging. He had been there almost a year and he had good days and bad days, but continued to be aggressive, kicking and biting his sisters and being destructive.

Hayley was still having problems at school and did not appear to be getting any sympathy there. The only suggestion made was that she go out of the fire door when her vocal tics were bad. We requested a statement but they said it was unnecessary in their opinion. The Tourette Syndrome (UK) Association suggested we ask for an assessment on whether or not she did need statementing, but the results of this can take up to six months and we simply had to wait.

Meanwhile, Nicholas was due to start infant school and we were worried that he would not settle, and that past experiences would be repeated. We consulted our GP again, as we felt that Nicholas also needed specialist help, but we sensed a change in his attitude. It became almost patronising, but he did agree to send Nicholas to a paediatrician.

Hayley was still experiencing many problems at school. She was being subjected to a lot of teasing because of her tics and vocalisations, and it was causing her a great deal of distress. We found her in her bedroom crying. "Why doesn't anybody like me? Why can't I be like everyone else?" and this made us feel totally helpless. But we managed to console her and carry on. Her medication was being increased and decreased at the hospital's request to try and help her, but it didn't seem to be working. The hospital suggested putting her on Sulpiride for a month, but nothing changed. She then ran away from school after much teasing and no understanding from any of the staff. We did our best to relieve things and try to reassure her, but that didn't work either.

In April 1996 Hayley's statement arrived, but it was a note 'in lieu' meaning that no help would be given at this time because of government cuts, which was of no use to Hayley, and, anyway, she was now at home and not attending school. We felt unsupported by both our GP and the hospital. We never seemed to get adequate answers to our questions about her behaviour, which we feel is so necessary. We asked our GP for a second opinion, which was reluctantly given, as he felt she was already getting the best of care. We were very unhappy. We were then told that the specialist he had in mind was no longer taking referrals. We complained to the Health Authority by letter, and suddenly the GP changed his mind and made the referral.

Nicholas is now also exhibiting more serious vocal and motor tics, which, when they began, had been put down to hay fever by our doctor. In August 1996, he injured himself badly, needing stitches in his head, because of a sudden tic movement. We were devastated. I cried, but what made matters worse was that my husband refused to believe Nicholas had the same condition as Hayley. He just could not face it, and I was angry and bitter that Nicholas' childhood was being taken away from him, just like Hayley's, and there was nothing we could do about it. Were we going to experience the same negative reaction from the authorities? Only time would tell. Society can be very cruel.

In July 1996, we had our second opinion and learnt from the consultant that Hayley has full blown Tourettes with the associated disorders of ADHD, OCD, and Conduct Disorder. At least we now knew that Hayley was not mad. He agreed to write a letter supporting our request for statementing. Secondary school was the next step for her and we spent many weeks writing to and visiting schools, talking to staff and doing our best to educate them about Hayley's condition. We found this exhausting, as we received no help and some schools didn't even bother to reply. We were struggling also with the knowledge that we both carried these faulty genes, so our emotions were torn. We felt very guilty for passing this on to our children. It became so bad that it was impossible for us to talk about it, or come to terms with it in any way.

On a visiting day to the secondary school we had chosen, Hayley was teased by two boys. She retaliated, lost her temper and swore, and ran off crying. I spoke to the head and was immediately told that, "We cannot have a child like Hayley at this school". We arranged an urgent meeting at the school to explain, but the statement had now to be changed to meet Hayley's increasing needs. She was ready to start school but only time would tell if things would work out. She was very apprehensive and didn't have any faith in the teachers, but her statementing was in place and she had two care assistants. She seemed to settle well with few problems and we were very relieved. All she ever needed was consistency, routine, and lots and lots of understanding. However, by the end of September the school informed us that they could no longer fund Hayley's lunch-time care. This is a part of the day when she most needs it and we were very upset. But it seemed the problem was one the school could not rectify, and we were out of time to appeal.

We decided to see a solicitor and found that it is illegal for the school to do this, because lunch-time is considered part of the school day. We asked for the statement to be amended to cover this period, but the head refused, insisting that Hayley would get only the classroom care. This was difficult for us to understand, as we believed her statement could be altered to include lunch and school activities, and we found collecting her at lunch-time – a four mile return journey – was too much for us. So, reluctantly, we had to agree to her being unsupervised during lunch-time.

An incident occurred where Hayley slapped a child for taunting her. Reports were taken from the other children present, but we felt that there was no concern on the school's part for Hayley's well-being. She sat alone in her bedroom, her anxiety level at its highest and her tics completely out of control. We had to do something quickly, but what? There had been so little help in the past and the school was unwilling to rectify any of the obstacles we encountered. We decided to keep her at home until the LEA did something. Our solicitor helped by gaining legal aid for us to take the LEA to court if the lunch-time care was not replaced. The LEA agreed to do this, however, and Hayley went back to school.

She went back to see the consultant at the hospital and her medication was changed. She was put on Prozac, which seemed to take the edge off her mood swings and temper tantrums, but she still appeared to be anxious and uptight.

In December 1996, with Christmas approaching, Hayley was experiencing a lot of dizziness, painful spasms, and was hyperventilating – all side effects of Prozac. Our doctor recommended that she come off the drug immediately. We called the consultant and he suggested that she stay at home until they could see her and stabilise her, and he was very understanding about what Hayley was going through. We told the school, but they didn't seem at all sympathetic. The consultant put her on a drug called Ritalin, and as time moved on, things seemed to improve. Haley was more confident, even radiant, and the hyperactivity was calming down. She was spending more time with the family since her aggression had decreased. Christmas was fine, and we were beginning to enjoy life, with Hayley obeying the rules we had laid down which were firm but fair.

However, Nicholas is now displaying the same pattern of behaviour in respect of school and again we are receiving the same uncaring attitude. We were actually told that we should be grateful that they were treating him like a normal child. We couldn't believe it!

January 13th was a day none of us will ever forget. We were expecting an arranged visit from social services, but to our horror we learned that outside agencies had raised concerns about our children's welfare and they had come to do a risk assessment. Apparently they believed that my husband and I were responsible in some way for our children's behaviour, and that this constituted child abuse on our part. They referred us to Section 47 of The Children's Act. We went into immediate panic. Were we going to lose our children because of a neurological disorder that these people did not want to understand? What was going to happen? And when? We asked for time to consult our solicitor, which they granted. We showed our solicitor the list we had been given of everything we could be accused of, from emotional to sexual abuse. He did not think they had a case, but since he didn't know the grounds they were working from, we were really at their mercy. During the following few days we seemed to slip into some kind of oblivion. The feeling of guilt was becoming too much to bear, but we had to put on a brave front for the children's sake, and somehow we managed it.

Nicholas has also been to the hospital and our fears were confirmed. He, too, has Tourette Syndrome, coupled with ADHD and Conduct Disorder. In a way, it was a relief to hear this, as it made our case against the risk assessment that much stronger. We discovered that our GP was one of the people who had brought these charges against us and we put in a complaint to the Health Authority. We then found another GP who seemed to be more understanding, and we also requested a change of educational psychologist. This may all seem very drastic, but we needed a team who were prepared to listen to us with an open mind. There was simply no room for negativity.

The effect of all this hanging over our heads was snowballing. Hayley was having more difficulty at school, with incidents nearly every day, and conflict between herself and her carers. On one occasion, she left the class after being told off and the carer did not go with her. Feeling unjustly punished, Hayley found a phone box and called us. We calmed her down, then called the school and asked them what was happening. Apparently no one was even aware that she was missing. The carer, it seemed, was doing other things. Another time she injured her arm when one of the schoolchildren pushed her over. Again, where was her carer?

The final straw came the following week when we received a call from the school to say that Hayley had been removed from class because she was making her hand bleed by dragging a key across it. Hayley explained to us that the taunting was getting her down and later that day she obviously reached breaking point and ran away. The school could not find her and we frantically looked for her ourselves. We eventually found her, face down in the road, muddy, cut, grazed, and in a state of shock. She flatly refused to go back to school, and just seemed to give up. We tried to be positive for her, but how much pressure were we expected to suffer? Did they have no idea of Hayley's disorder? The school refused a meeting with us, and the LEA granted only one hour's home tuition a day.

Mainstream education had let us down, so we approached a special school in London for ADHD sufferers. The consultant had also, by this time, recommended Nicholas for statementing, and we were waiting for the results of that. We attended a meeting of the Risk Assessment Board on 3 February 1997. We were very relieved to find that they considered there was no real evidence of abuse, due to the fact that both our children are medically diagnosed, but they stressed that the concerns that had been raised had to be acknowledged and investigated, and that it was unfortunate that we had been subjected to such pressure and distress. It would have been a different story if the authorities had just gone ahead and placed our children on the At Risk Register. Whose job is it to protect children from the professionals?

We have tried everything we could to deal with our children's problems, taking one day at a time, and not aiming too high. Every parent's approach to this kind of thing must be a unique one. What will work for one will not necessarily work for another. Where possible, parents should try to keep some sort of life for themselves, as there *is* life beyond Tourettes. And if all else fails, try humour. We will never give up correcting people who are continually wrong about these disorders, and we are ready for another round in the ring. To say that TS does not alter family life is the biggest understatement in the world. You have to learn to function as a normal everyday family, but with differences.

Looking back over the eight years since these disorders first manifested themselves in our two children, right out of the blue, we have made many mistakes. We have punished and bribed them in order to try to make them behave, but they were physically unable to do it. We have been unable to talk together as a couple because of our sense of guilt, not to mention the added stress and pressure placed on us by the professionals. We are continually amazed at the power these people can have over us. But the problems, and the people we have encountered along this painful journey will help to take us from strength to strength, rebuilding all the time the bricks that got broken. They say some people are born to survive. AND WE WILL!

JUST LIKE YOU

Jonathon Jones

To the most beautiful girl in the world, Charlotte Kviste.

My childhood up to about the age of eight was pretty darn good, looking back. This was mainly due to the fact that I was above averagely clever, and was just one in a sea of many faces. I was just like everyone else. I got on well with everyone, and I even found some enjoyment from sport, even though I wasn't very good at it. Then everything seemed to very gently unravel.

If I became stressed I would get a tightening in and around my head, and I can remember whacking our kitchen door back against the end of the work surface, until I had rent a gaping hole in it. I wasn't into destruction, but I had to satisfy this tension within me, and that seemed the only way to do it. I would get these mad moments, and then they would be gone and I would go back outside to play with my friends, acting the clown, just like everyone else. In fact, I thought I was no different from anyone else, so I didn't worry about it unduly. Anyway, I was still one of the highest performers at school and still pretty popular and it wasn't getting in the way of my life, so who cared?

Then I began to say faintly odd things – things like, "I like sticking it in with someone I know", and I would add rhythm to it by banging my hands against any surface or object that was in close proximity. Then I made it into a little ditty and directed it at authority figures, in one case my mother, and in another, two teachers at school. I would antagonise my mother at every opportunity, and I didn't know why. It was just something I had to do. The pulling out of my genitals came soon after, and this is one action I still find difficult to keep in check to this day.

I started to become unpopular with those directly around me because of my increasingly bizarre nature, which included poking out my tongue at my peers, making V-signs with my hands at strangers, and exhibiting vocal tics such as tongue clicking and grunting, and a whole host of other silly things that just sort of replaced themselves, one after the other. I spent a lot of time running away from angry, provoked children. Not a great time, all in all. I did learn, however, to cry on tap, which kept me out of beatings, but which did nothing for my street-cred. I was soon to be an outcast. There were some that would still befriend me, but in the main, real friends were not an option. I never got used to that.

By this time, I had begun to experience rages. These were usually single, isolated events – blots on an otherwise clear landscape, but they were frightening all the same. During these episodes I would throw things about, shout and swear, and generally behave in a fashion that wasn't particularly befitting an otherwise smart little lad. I was heading down the slippery slope that would characterise my life with what I now know as the condition called the Tourette Syndrome.

I was becoming increasingly difficult and unmanageable to the degree that I became known as something of a problem child. My mother blamed me more and more for her friends not wanting to come and visit, which made me even more tense, so I would act up all the more. So it became a vicious circle, literally. At about this time, aged ten, I was laying into my mother with an unceasing and monotonous regularity, both on the physical and the mental level. I was swearing at her using the most basic of terms. If she walked into the room she would be called, amongst other things, a stupid cow – a bitch – an old slapper, or crap face. I had picked up these words from around the place and would bandy them about with as much vitriol as I could muster, and I never quite knew why I was doing it – I just had to!

Throughout all of this I had found a true friend in the form of my father, Vernon, who was an endless fount of wisdom and succour. He was a rock, that man. What can I say about him? He was, quite simply, the best friend I will ever have. I would drive him daily to the edge of despair with my unceasing chatter and constant ramblings, but he seemed to take it all in good spirit. You see, we were both broken in some way. He had suffered a massive stroke when I was only six months old, which debilitated him, and we needed each other to find a way of remedying that which was not quite right. We had both had experiences of normality, but were now in a situation where all those things we had come to believe in were now fast-fading memories, and my youth, coupled with his wisdom, just about got us through. I loved that man!

So our partnership was cemented and my every waking moment was spent with him. He was a tower of strength to me and I was an injection of fresh air to him, and it worked quite well. He was a ray of sunshine in a world that seemed to be getting bleaker by the day, and it didn't seem to matter how tense or anxious any given situation would make me, I would always find sanctuary with him. I never once took any of my rages out on him. He just quietly understood without question, and to this day I still don't fully comprehend it. It was love without question, love without barriers, love without pretence. It was love in its absolute and purest form, and I still miss him.

At this time I was made to sit the Eleven Plus exam at school, ostensibly to get me into one of the more select schools. To be honest, all that I was interested in was getting back to the safety of home and the informative chats and surreal dialogue that by now had become commonplace between Vernie and me. But in saying that, I did enjoy the test in itself, for it opened up to me the fascinating world of verbal reasoning. I liked the questions and the layout of the text, and it introduced me to my now almost legendary obsession with number. I was still terrible at mathematics, but numbers, they were different! I liked the discipline of the times tables, particularly the nine times table, which had a morbid fascination for me, and nine is still my favourite number to this day.

Verbal reasoning was a nice package. It was more than simple arithmetic but not as tricky as full-blown mathematics. It became something of a fad for me at that time. I very quickly worked my way through all the books of that nature in the local bookshop. Then, in very much the same way as I do now, I dumped this obsession and moved on to the next one, which happened to be saying words backwards, which I still do today. It's quite a party trick!

That's the very nature of all this and something I find unsettling and disturbing. I have absolutely no staying power of any kind whatsoever. I seem to be forever searching for something that doesn't exist; a way, any way, any thing, that will sustain my interest for even the slightest amount of time. Unless, of course, I am genuinely interested in the subject, then my staying power is slightly better, though not what you might class as spectacular in any sense of the word. I have had a guitar for the best part of ten years, and when I am being shown how to play it, or I am playing with someone else, I seem to be galvanised into action. But when it is down to me, and me alone, nothing ever seems to get done.

Tourette Syndrome is a highly visible complaint, and as a society we are strung out on the whole idea of aesthetics, and we fail to grasp the subtleties of humanity. We just skirt the surface of what is truly there. We live in a deeply superficial world where image is the key, and what's under the surface is only truly evaluated if the person on the exterior passes a whole series of banal tests; and that is a damning indictment on life in general. We have a tendency to see anyone who is slightly different as being not just a threat, but actually being of less value as well. Living with a disability enables me to not only get behind the façade and see what's really there, ie the person, it also enables me to really feel what may be going on within that person. So the one truly great aspect of my life so far with TS, is the ongoing ability to fully appreciate and empathise with others and what they may be living through on a day-to-day basis. So in that sense, living with TS has been nothing short of a godsend.

Having passed the Eleven Plus, I began at Reading Grammar School in

September of 1985, at the ripe old age of eleven. I didn't really care much for it, but decided to just get on with it, since it wasn't as if I had a choice. The first year was okay and I was pretty much like everyone else; albeit a more ticcy version. However, this was where my terror ride began, and there would be no safety belts in place and no crash barriers to soften the blows. This would be a journey into the unknown.

The second year was by far one of the most testing times in my life. I remember throwing one of my friend's schoolwork out of a window, just for the hell of it. That, to most people, would seem callous or cruel, but to someone with TS, it is all too familiar. It usually begins with some kind of tightening inside, a kind of mounting up of tension, and the only thing that will ease the vice is to release the tension … somehow. That can mean anything from a vocal outburst, to hitting or kicking, effing and blinding, or, as in this case, destroying someone else's chance of revising and passing a test. It is something that defies logic, something that just has to be done, regardless of the personal consequences. As long as the immediate situation is remedied, then to hell with everyone else seems to be the order of the day.

For a while, both teachers and fellow pupils were very supportive of my situation, and me, but this didn't last long. This is where I pretty much began to lose the plot. I would go to specific places on the school site where I could just be alone with 'this thing', and I started talking to people who weren't there. I was always aware that there was no one there; it was just that inventing characters made me feel special, made me feel wanted. They listened to me and valued what I had to say. I would create a whole audience and have them in fits of laughter with my crazy banter and wild reflex-quick repartee. I had found myself to be so alternative in mainstream society, that I had no real outlet for my brand of humour. But this was perfect. Not only did I have an outlet, thus rendering me virtually stress free, I also had some kind (albeit a crude form) of acceptance.

This started to get a stranglehold on me. I had about three places that I would disappear to, all self-contained. I could sit and grumble, mumble, shout, grimace, and spin round to my heart's content, because at this stage in the game I was exhibiting full blown TS symptoms, both vocal and non-vocal. These included: finger tapping against any object, throat clearing, strange utterances, shouting "hey" at inopportune times, touching myself intimately, swearing indiscriminately, fiddling with my nose and ears, eye winking/blinking, facial grimacing, nostril flaring, tongue clicking, stretching and shutting eyes, removing shoes to count toes … the list goes on … It would not be true to say that these all happened at the same time, because they didn't. They would just sort of replace each other as time wore on. But in saying that, I could sometimes go for weeks without one single symptom, which always gave me the hope that I had cracked this thing.

Sadly, this was never the case.

Back to obsessional thought. I was beginning to exhibit strange and irrational behaviours, for example, wearing underpants in the bath due to the misplaced fear that faeces would fall into the water if I didn't. This took two years to work through. Then I went through a period of holding on to faeces for as long as possible. My record was nine days, after which the local doctor had to come and administer an enema. That completely cured me of that one, for it presented oceans of the very stuff I had been fearful of getting rid of and worked on the level of a primitive kind of confrontational therapy. I can still vividly remember both the sensation and the realisation of having been trapped with an irrational fear. And that's just it – I know that most of my obsessions are totally invalid, but I just have to go through the motions anyway (no pun intended).

I was midway through my third year at secondary school when my arch enemy arithmemania presented itself. It made my life completely unbearable at times. I also embarked upon my 'close shave' episodes as well which, frankly, frightened the life out of me. I remember my mother being out in the garden with me and running indoors to answer the phone, leaving me unattended with an electric mower. I would go up to it, flip it over, and then almost dare myself to put my fingers into the blade. It would be like the fight between good and evil. I knew that the chances were that something would hold me back, but sometimes I really wasn't quite sure whether I would get out of the situation unscathed, and that really put the frighteners on at times. I would also wait by the side of the road, and the moment a car whizzed by I would walk out into the traffic, just skirting the vehicle in doing so. The feeling of the rush of air against my legs and lower body, coupled with the nudge of the car against me, gave me a short, sharp burst of nervous energy that I loved. I didn't have any friends at this time, so it made up for something, I can tell you.

At the age of fourteen I began to see Robert Williams, a youth counsellor, ostensibly to talk through why I was exhibiting such anti-social behaviour. He and I sort of clicked, and for the next two and a half years I had an outlet for my bizarre sense of humour and demonstrative patterns of behaviour. I left school at seventeen and my visits to Mr Williams stopped.

I then started to see a new counsellor, who, in turn, would become one of my closest friends. His name was Rhys and he worked for an organisation called Number Five, which was based in Reading, and I saw him once a week. I was still almost completely suppressed in public, save for a few odd winks and blinks here and there, but he granted me a new kind of serenity. He wasn't so probing and certainly wasn't indifferent to my true plight. I think he understood that there was probably something of a sub-plot going on within me, and the irony was that it has only been in the last year or so that I have shared this ghastly secret with him, and he has been completely supportive. God bless you, buddy. Rhys was a cut above the rest, and I ended up using his service as a surrogate friendship, instead of a counselling device, but he allowed it because there was something special between us. Two kindred spirits, like two minds impacting. All good stuff. I stopped seeing him when I was about twenty. I guess that at the time I felt that I had outgrown him, as a counsellor, I mean. Then my twenty-first birthday came around and I knew that I wanted him there. Not much had occurred in my life since I had stopped seeing him, but I knew also that he would turn up that night in a different capacity, and I was correct. He turned up as a friend. That evening something strange occurred. I dropped all pretence with him, but only him. He *was* my friend and he *did* care. Boy, was that a defining moment!

At around this time I joined the local gym to get myself in shape. I was in a right state, but the truth was I needed an outlet for this thing – somewhere I could just go and get it all out, and it worked well. I would sometimes go four or five times a week and work myself into the ground, for it meant that for the remainder of the day I was almost tic-free, which was f...... fantastic! I couldn't get enough of it and for the first time in my life I felt free. So it became a regular event. Going to the gym took over my whole life and gave me an outlet for all my excessive and obsessive behaviour. For instance, it allowed me my love of numbers, for there were sets, and repetitions within sets, and there was a clock on the bikes and the treadmills, and I could count in time with it. Sometimes I would close my eyes and count in my head, then open my eyes and see if I had been correct in my counting. Usually I was only one or two seconds out either way, much to my relief.

And then I saw her. Her name was Charlotte Kviste and, boy, was she beautiful. Eyes so wide and so deep you could lose yourself looking into them. She moved with such grace and elegance that I could hardly catch my breath when she was around. She was heaven-sent. One hell of a classy lady! But in the eight months that she was around I didn't get to speak to her once. This was when I knew something was drastically wrong. When she was around, my heart would flutter, but I was useless. She would get me all nervous and then it would start. The throat clearing, the twitches, the vocal mannerisms, and then I would be afraid to go and talk to her in case she laughed at me and killed whatever shred of confidence I had left. I never did get to talk to her and have lived with that biggest and most painful of regrets ever since. I have never before or since experienced those feelings, and I definitely know now, what I thought I knew then – that I loved that woman!

After that, I had to find out what this thing was. It had bugged me before but it had never caused me to feel such 'heart ripped out' pain, so I had to find out what it was. It was something of a quest. I searched for an age, and then I found it. It was nearly a year afterwards, and it was by chance. I was mindlessly flicking through the TV channels late at night when I came across someone who did exactly what I did, albeit in a more exaggerated fashion. It was a programme made by the eminent neurologist, Dr Oliver Sacks, and it really hit me where I lived. I cried like a baby that night with a mixture of relief and heartfelt gladness that I was not alone. Not only were there others out there, it had a name as well. Having discovered this, I was in the library, in bookshops, on the Internet. I purchased a couple of books by Dr Sacks, namely, *The Man who Mistook his Wife for a Hat* and *An Anthropologist on Mars*. They were perfect – I was on my way.

It was a great comfort to know that I was not suffering alone, and I felt I was in good company. I sat in the middle of town and from my prime vantage point I would try and spot other Touretters and was surprised at what I found. Within weeks I had found a 'super-Touretter' as in one of Dr Sacks' books, and numerous others with Tourettic imbalance. I was in GREAT company! Everyone needs to feel they are not alone, even a confirmed loner like me. It's not so that you can fit in, but a need to know that others do empathise with you, and that in itself is a wonderful thing. You never tire of that. Never.

Now I faced the incredibly arduous task of trying to convince my GP that this is what I had. If you can imagine climbing up a mountainside in flip-flops, then that goes some way towards it. It was a nightmare. Firstly, I went to see another doctor (who shall be nameless), who told me I was nothing but an attention seeker with an overactive imagination, and that I was wasting both a good appointment and his time … BASTARD!! Then I gave up for a while. It upset me, to be honest. It had taken a great deal of courage to pluck up the confidence to go and tell him what I felt, and he simply pooh-poohed what I was saying, and that felt like a kick up the arse!

I immediately called the Tourette Syndrome Association and got through to a really nice man, Roy Hillard, who not only listened to me, but also understood a lot of what I was saying, which was a much-needed boost at a time when my spirits were at a low ebb. He gave me the courage to go back to my own doctor and implore him to believe me, which at last he did. But because I was darn good at suppressing my symptoms, he really had to take me on my word, and God bless him, because he did just that. An appointment was made for me to see Dr Hugh Rickards in Birmingham and the whole process began to take form.

The day arrived, 21 October 1999, and I was finally diagnosed with TS. I cried with relief that day – there really is a God. I was very worried that I would get there and be symptomless again, but again, thank God, everything that could possibly go wrong, went wrong that day. I almost missed the train at Reading, then it was late getting to Birmingham, then nobody knew where Edgbaston was – it was a f...... nightmare. When I finally got to the hospital I was a screaming lunatic. I was literally barking and shouting in the waiting room. I had to ask to be put into a smaller room at one point, as I felt I was going to explode with tension, and continued to tic away like a good 'un in one of the interview rooms to howls of laughter and derision from the waiting room. That upset me, which made me do it all the more, so diagnosis was not going to be much of a problem. What did surprise me though, was how young Dr Rickards was. I was expecting someone a lot older with a noticeable paunch and half moon specs – like Nigel Hawthorn in a greeny beige cardie. Well, I got the cardie right! But here was this youngish-looking doctor and it threw me for a minute. He was good at his job, though, and he made my visit to the hospital a short, yet, thankfully, most welcome one.

So here I am, many weeks later. It's now 22 December 1999, and I have been on Sulpiride for two months. I take one tablet before I go to sleep at night, and aside from the slightest of tics, I am practically normal. It feels great. It's bizarre really, because this is how I must have felt for the first eight years of my life, unthreatened by this thing. But that's not to say that I'll become complacent, because I won't. There is a tendency in society to forget where you've come from when you have passed through tempestuous times into calmer waters. I have no intention of doing such a thing. I still have TS, even though now it has decreased ten-fold and I am not ashamed to let it be known. This is my story so far.

~

This story would not have been possible without the help of the following people: my mother, Sadie Eileen Jones; Eric Clapton, my inspiration – a true survivor; Oliver Sacks, for giving me the first glimmer of hope; Dr Martin Bates, for being there; Rhys Ridgwell, a true friend when I needed one; Chris Mansley, a bright light who illuminated my darkest day; Roy Hillard; Stephen Pashley, who helped me write this story; Richard Baly, a real good Samaritan; Charles Rampton; Ian Judd, and of course, my dearest friend and father, Vernon George Jones (1917 – 1997).

LIGHT AT THE END OF THE TUNNEL

Peter Maisey

At the outset of my story, don't expect to read horrifying accounts of child neglect or abuse, of being ostracised by my peers, of social isolation, of being totally out of control. It didn't happen. Statistically, I am Joe Average – state educated – one wife – three children – a job. So why am I writing this down? Partly to satisfy the request of someone else, but mostly to allow me to explore more of what being a member of the TS club means to me.

After forty years of not knowing why I suffered various muscular and vocal tics, I was diagnosed as suffering from Tourette Syndrome. I think the impact of finding out has only slowly dawned on me, mainly as a result of talking with a counsellor over the last twelve months. If people ask, "Why do you do that?", then at last, after so many years, I can tell them. Those four words, "I can tell them" have a double meaning. I now have an answer, and probably more importantly, I can now talk about it. When I didn't know, I couldn't, or wouldn't, talk about it. That change is a revelation.

To put everything that follows into some kind of perspective, I suppose I'd first better describe both the visible and invisible characteristics of my TS. Simply put, I suffer from a desire to contract my muscles – muscles around the eyes, the face generally, shoulders, stomach, legs, everywhere. Not all of them all of the time, but all of them some of the time. And then there are the vocal tics. It's that simple.

I have no recollection of a sudden realisation that I was a twitcher. I suppose, on the basis of what others have said, I started about the age of eight or nine, or was it ten? I have no real idea, and it's not something I've ever discussed in detail with my parents. Nor do I want to, for reasons discussed later. The assumption was always that there were external influences affecting my life, and my reaction to them was muscular twitches.

What is being a TS sufferer like? Perhaps the best description I'm aware of, when talking to non-sufferers (I confess I've never discussed the issue with another sufferer), is to ask them why they breathe, and can they stop, and what happens if they try and stop. The muscles that contract and expand the lungs run on 'automatic' and although we might be able to stop them for a while, we can't do it for long, and in the end we are left gasping violently for breath. That's not an entirely accurate description of TS, because I think the word 'compelling' applies to TS, whereas 'involuntary' is a better description for breathing. But I think to a non-sufferer it's a suitable analogy.

You might also watch people holding a small baby. Have you noticed how they start swaying gently back and forth? Now, they do stop, of course, but they do have a compulsion to do it. And when they hand the baby back, they stop. If only we could hand back our baby ...

My trigger? My medical history was often suspected of being the cause of my tics. Born a twin, I had talapes (club foot). Many hours of therapy, splints, electrotherapy, operations, later, I was 'cured'. Cured, anyway, to the extent that I can walk and run. I once did a marathon, and still run cross country, and orienteer. I'm not much good, but that's beside the point. I remember very little of those hospital visits, despite the fact that I sometimes attended two or three times a week.

The last operation? I was about ten, and at that stage I do know that I exhibited muscular twitches, mainly because another patient in the ward asked me why I did it. I think it was eyes at the time. I can just about remember certain bits; wheelchair races around the ward, not going to school, the plaster coming off, the delight of scratching my leg again without the aid of a knitting needle.

Was the arrival of my youngest sister when I was aged ten, of significance? This was an option at the time. I'd had so much attention as the poor little boy suffering all that medical attention, that perhaps my tics were an attempt to recapture the attention that the arrival of my sister had taken away. It all seemed pretty plausible at the time.

I have subsequently read that trauma, shock, etc have been added to the list of possible triggers. The suggestion is that whilst an individual may have the genetic predisposition towards TS, a traumatic trigger is needed to set if off. If this is true, then in my case, it seems to have been more a war of attrition than a cataclysmic event.

How did my parents react? As I've already indicated, my memory of things past tends to be rather poor. I'm not sure if this is a defence mechanism against all the trauma of hospital visits, but I do remember a visit to a psychiatrist when I was about twelve, but he was not specifically a child psychiatrist. I remember opening the door for him, as he arrived at the same time as I did, and I managed to (typically) keep control for the short time I was with him. He said I'd grow out of it by the time I was fifteen. Obviously, he didn't really know what he was talking about. Much later, I asked my mother about it, and she admitted that she felt he wasn't the right person for me to see at the time. But in those days you didn't argue with your doctor. You knew your place.

Relationships with my parents and my siblings were, if there is such a thing, normal. We were, and still are, what can be described as a close family. Although we don't live in close proximity, we don't live that far apart either, yet visits aren't that regular. However, we do have the ability to continue the conversation that we had six months earlier as if we'd seen each other only yesterday. I have no recollection of my siblings ever referring to my tics, to me, or to anyone else. They seem to accept me for who I am, warts and all. Nor did they ever confide in me if anyone else ever commented to them about me, adversely or otherwise.

Holding it in … Given the right circumstances I can hold things in check, probably enough to fool you, for a short period of time, into thinking I don't have nervous twitches. But like breathing, I can't hold it for long. And I have reached the point where I don't really try any more. Accept me as I am, or it's your loss. I have plenty to offer you, and if my tics put you off, then you lose. Of course, that's a front. I do have a concern if people are affected by my tics, and I do try and stop for a while. However, since I have been diagnosed with TS, it has become more important that people understand.

It would be the simplest thing in the world to become a recluse. If other people weren't around, would I have a problem? Of course the tics are debilitating, but how much of what I personally perceive to be problems are the result of having to mix with others. Society places many demands on us, but starting with a penalty makes it much more difficult. Sidelong glances, whispered comments, people moving away – or so I think – the refused offer to go on a school trip with my son's class.

My wife tells me this is not true. Is she oblivious to it all, or am I paranoid? Paranoia makes it all that much easier to justify. What's worse, contrary to what the previous paragraph might suggest, I have no great problem mixing with others, but I do have a nagging fear of embarrassing my wife or children in front of their friends. I have always been petrified that my children would be ridiculed by their peers at school because of me. It doesn't matter whether it's true or not. It's what I perceive to be true that counts. I have raised this issue with my wife in connection with socialising with her work colleagues. She says she would not take me to any function where people would make an issue of it, and so far she's been true to her word. She does see the double-takes from other people, but she also sees that they ignore my tics and get on with socialising.

But then I notice that groups of people from the working and social circles I move in also have get-togethers. I am not invited. Am I being excluded because of TS? Others are excluded because they aren't friends, so why can't I accept that. Because maybe, just maybe, I am not seen as a friend because I have TS, and they don't want any weirdos in their gang. Paranoia – my panacea.

Holding back. I've done a fair bit in my life, probably more than most people. So is it fair to say that TS held me back? I think the answer has to be a guarded "yes", even before I knew what caused my tics. I consider myself to be an underachiever. For several years I made a point of telling my boss at my annual job appraisal, that I wasn't interested in promotion because I was happy as I was. I didn't explain why, but a recent comment I came across summed the situation up very nicely. "You think you are satisfied with your job. In reality you are just afraid of change."

It's all down to being in control. If I'm not in control, it's nothing to do with me. If I lose control, I walk away. Promotion would mean something new, and something new equates to loss of control. It's *me* that has held me back, not TS. Maybe I have used it as a scapegoat. However, now that I know what's going on, perhaps I will be able to let go occasionally. But somehow, I don't think that's very likely.

Support. I'm married with three kids. The kids had no choice about having a father with TS, but my wife certainly had a choice about marrying me. At the time I did not suffer from vocal tics. But it was my wife who finally persuaded me to do something about my affliction after the vocal tics began – albeit some ten years later. In fact, she wanted me to do something much earlier, but it took me that long to find the right questions to ask my doctor, and that long to get him to do something by referring me to a neurologist.

My wife was always prepared to be supportive, and for a long time tried to discuss my problem with me. It was always me who wasn't prepared, wasn't able to discuss anything. How could I discuss something over which I had no control, nor any understanding? When I started seeing a counsellor, she came with me to give some insight from her point of view. I was quite surprised to discover that her aim had been to get me some benefit by encouraging me to see a specialist. She had never been too embarrassed to be seen in public with me, it was me who had assumed this. I think the discovery that I was a TS sufferer was as much a revelation to her as it was to me.

Good days … bad days … I can't say my TS is as severe as I've heard some suffer. But I do have days that are better than others. Stress plays a fairly significant part in a bad day. I don't restrict the definition of stress to the mental pressure we all seem to suffer nowadays because of our busy lifestyles, I also include illness. I'm a fairly fit person who indulges in running in various forms, and years of experience tells me that a bad run usually means I'm sickening for something.

Winding down at the end of the day helps relieve the symptoms; stretching out on the sofa, hypnotised by the television, or reading a book. However, this has a downside as well. To wind down completely means that I don't want to talk to anyone – not fair on my wife and the youngest of our three sons (the other two have flown the nest). Sometimes I'm a gossip, a chatterbox who won't stop talking. I can't stand the silences. But if I'm wound up, the conversation can be very short and sharp. It might seem to others that I can't be bothered to talk, but the truth is that it's sometimes very hard work. My social conscience says socialise: my selfish side says keep it short.

Subsequent to writing this section, I became ill with a heavy cold and its associated symptoms. I had always suspected that my TS became worse when I was ill, and to an extent I realised that still held true. However, it also dawned on me that much of the apparent worsening is perceived and not real. It suggests that when I am ill, I am less able to handle my TS. It gets on top of me more, and I wonder if this leads to a downward spiral.

Today's special offer! I have a repertoire of tics to choose from. When I wake up in the morning, I don't know what the selection for today is going to be. It's usually yesterday's, although it can take a few minutes after waking to get going. Sometimes I wake and realise I'm not twitching – if only – then they start, almost as if I had deliberately started them. Sometimes I add to my repertoire, but as I get older that is becoming rare and I select from one I've already used. This gives the impression that I only suffer one tic at any given time, but it would be more accurate to say that one tic dominates at any given time. Switching the dominating tic sometimes occurs during the day. When it does, I notice the pattern is usually the mixing of two tics, one gradually phasing out, or decreasing in dominance, the other phasing in. I see the phasing in tic as an unpleasant event. And the phasing out tic as losing something I've grown to know … better the devil you know …

It's the vocal tics that get me down the most. It's because these impact more forcefully on other people. And, in truth, if it weren't for the audible nature of this particular affliction, I probably wouldn't have bothered to do anything about the whole thing. It's easy to look away, but more difficult to close your ears. And it's the vocal tics that have generated most comments over the years. I know they annoy people. I know they don't like it, and I'd love to be able to stop or even switch to a muscular tic, but I don't have that control. There's that word 'control' again. TS is one aspect of my life over which I have no control. Is this why I need to have control over all the other aspects?

Out of control is all. I've always thought that I don't like change. But the truth is probably that I don't like change that I have no control over. I have, for example, worked overseas – a huge upheaval. But it was my decision to do it and I was supported by my wife. If she had displayed any kind of negative attitude, I'd probably have pulled my usual trick of walking away. It may seem that I'm not interested, or can't be bothered, but I'm not in control, so I'm walking away.

And mine is the kind of job where change is part and parcel of everyday life. It's not a regular nine to five situation with the day laid out, although I try to make it as much like that as possible. It's often that I lurch from one crisis to another, often cursing the stupidity of my customers. There are often days when I'd like to do something mundane, something regular, but I know I would soon get bored. So, in reality, the job matches the way I am to some extent. Plenty of variation within the limits of my knowledge, which is essential to ensure that I don't hit my boredom threshold.

I do seem to have a low boredom threshold. I can't handle monolithic slabs of work. However, it may not seem that way if you ask my colleagues at work. This is because I have developed a strategy to handle it. I break the job up into smaller and smaller chunks. I am very much a linear thinker. One thing, and only one thing at a time. I'm not sure if this is how I would be without TS, or whether it's a reaction to an already overloaded brain. Is all this a suggestion of a mild attention deficiency rather than a low boredom threshold? Or are they one and the same?

When I think back, I find that memories are something I'm very short of. Perhaps it is a protective barrier of some kind, but I don't think so. However, the following comments have to be considered with this in mind. Did I suffer as a kid from others? Surprisingly, looking back, no, or not that I remember. Nor did any teacher ever raise the issue with me directly. I don't know if they did with my parents. Actually, that's not entirely true, I do recollect one teacher taking exception to a vocal tic, but only because she thought I was just mucking about. At the age of nine or ten, I wasn't in a position to defend or explain myself to her because of her power as a teacher, and her lack of knowledge and/or experience of TS.

Parental comments? Of course there were. Such as, "stop that", to begin with. And I was aware that my maternal grandparents were concerned. The only adverse verbal sideswipe I can ever remember was when my father stated that he could never take me to an auction. When I went to an interview to get on a degree course, I had the habit of shaking my head at that time, and my mother commented later that she hoped I hadn't done it at the interview. But, of course, I had. How could I stop? I was offered the place, anyway, based on my academic achievements.

Peer comments? Again, there were. The most frustrating thing was not knowing the answer when people asked what the problem was, not that many did. Did I have a traumatic birth? How would I know? Possibly my early operations and electrotherapy triggered the whole thing. But I didn't know the answer.

Clear as mud. The more I think and talk, the less clear things become. Most recently, the only real attempt by the medical fraternity to help me was an appointment with a neurosurgeon – a fifteen-minute chat that led to a diagnosis of TS – yes, just fifteen minutes! This was followed by a series of visits to a counsellor.

Counselling. Having suffered from TS symptoms for over forty years, and seemingly getting worse, it was my wife who made me do something about it. It's not true to say that I'd not done anything in the past, but medical profession apathy/ignorance and the failure of hypnotherapy didn't make me optimistic. I recognised that I hadn't pursued all possibilities, but I also recognised why – all the time unexplored avenues still existed, there was some hope. To discover that the last one might be a cul-de-sac, and that I was doomed to suffer for life, was, quite frankly, frightening.

So one final attempt was on. Choosing my words and doctor very carefully was imperative. So I selected the doctor most likely to show an interest and didn't so much as ask a question, as make a statement. "I want to know if …" I can tell you that this was a very hard thing to do. Partly because it wasn't something I found easy to talk about, even to a doctor. But mainly because I felt that if the net result was that there was no hope, how would I cope? All the time I did not pursue a possible cure, the hope of a possible cure was always there.

The net result was a visit to a neurologist, and that led to an opportunity to talk to a counsellor. After a year of regular visits, am I cured? Of course not. Was it worth it? Definitely. For while accepting that TS was never going to go away, I found it extremely valuable in getting to grips with who I am and why I am that person. Having explained how TS affected me physically, we went on to explore its psychological impact. I try to be gregarious, but there I sat, arms covering my chest and lower face and with my legs crossed, as defensive a body posture as you can get. I also had to answer, "don't know" to many early questions, not necessarily because there was no answer, or I wouldn't answer, but because I couldn't answer. I'd never thought that deeply about my problem, and forty years of not talking about a problem is a hard habit to break. So I had two problems to overcome. Firstly, I had to start thinking seriously, and secondly, I had to make myself talk.

My wife's visit for the second session was very important to me, as I wanted the counsellor to hear the view of another person. I was surprised that she said she'd pushed me into this for my benefit. If I'm honest, I thought her motives were purely selfish, but it took a load off my mind, enabling me to get a good deal more from counselling, while my wife, hopefully, would also benefit from anything I gained.

After a number of sessions it became obvious that I needed to feel that I was in control of as many aspects of my life as possible, as I have already intimated. This, I assume, is because TS is the one aspect of my life that I cannot control. So the overall result seems to be, that: control is essential, I am scared of change and I ignore (or walk away) from things I cannot control. And I keep telling myself that this is really quite dumb. I work with computers – big computers – two thousand users – from Madrid to Moscow. On average, every eighteen months, we have a major software or hardware upheaval, and we start from scratch. So I *can* and *do* handle change. I just don't enjoy it. The walking away is obviously not so easy, but I manage it. In a way, I suspect it's also a method of handling stressful situations. The stress lies in my lack of control of the situation.

The next major event was to try hypnotherapy again. I'd often wondered, if I can sleep calmly, how deeply buried was my desire to twitch – such a painful word for me. I assumed the previous failure of hypnotherapy was due to my lack of desire to make use of it, but with a little more knowledge of the cause of TS, I now realise it was doomed to fail. It is very difficult for me to lie still, for a start, and only towards the end of the session did I even begin to relax, so the twenty minutes each patient was allocated was not enough. I still feel that the process could be useful, but I don't know how to use it to greater effect.

At the start of the counselling sessions it was extremely difficult for me to talk about my symptoms. That would have meant admitting I had a problem, and for forty years I had never talked about it to anyone. The reality was that I could easily become a recluse. Socialising is difficult, but I just have to get on with it. Maybe I should walk up to people and say, "I am a f...... TS sufferer. Now that you know, I'd like to stop swearing and have a decent conversation."

Since I started seeing a counsellor, it became so much easier to talk about TS. I did talk to a couple of long-term work colleagues about it once I was diagnosed as a sufferer (sufferer? – why use that word? – because that's what I do – suffer). I physically shook as I talked to them, that's how hard it was. Their sense of revelation was interesting to watch and they were pleased that I had confided in them. They subsequently asked, from time to time, how I was progressing, and I consider the interest neither ghoulish nor academic. But I chose those who I confided in very carefully.

Six months and several counselling sessions later, I decided to raise the TS issue with my boss at my annual career appraisal, and I could not believe how much easier talking about it had become, though it still took some planning as to how to broach the subject. The main result of our meeting, for me, was to discover that he felt there was no need to explain TS to my colleagues, because it did not impact on their working relationship with me, and that there would be no benefit. I felt this to be a positive rather than a negative attitude.

The counselling is coming to an end now. Was it worth the effort? I still have TS and it was never intended as a cure. But I am now much clearer about who and what I am. I no longer feel quite the despair I have felt in the past. I have TS in much better perspective. It has given me a desire to move forward, to explore my symptoms, their cause, and a possible improvement. My self-esteem is much greater than at the start, but there was only one way for it to go back then. BUT I STILL HAVE TS …

What ifs … If there was ever a futile occupation, it was the post-mortem after an exam. My classmates would all stand around discussing how they'd answered a particular question. Of course, it was an ego trip for the brighter kids, but by that time it was too late. They were discussing worthless 'what ifs'. And that's the way I now feel about TS. I could ask whether I'd have done anything differently had I known about TS earlier. How about the question, "Would I have had children if I'd known I had TS with its hereditary overtones?" To understand how futile this kind of questioning is, consider this. My eldest son had a master's degree in Theoretical Physics at the age of twenty-one, and is on his way to a second Master's in Applied Maths as he is approaching twenty-two. My second son, not so academically gifted, is a member of a local band on their way up. He sets up the sound system, tunes the guitars, and can play any of the guitar parts. My third son, nine years old, just gives us a lot of enjoyment. They each have a lot to offer the world!!!

Dilemma. I do have one outstanding dilemma. I haven't told my parents of the diagnosis because I don't want them attaching any blame to themselves, hereditary or not. But I do blame myself for the fact that my children have milder symptoms of TS. I can't say it's nothing to do with me, because it's everything to do with me. Okay, I can't turn back the clock, but that doesn't make the blame go away.

Light at the end of the tunnel. This is not the end of the line. I still plan to continue my attempts to get to grips with my situation, and to try and improve my control over the symptoms of TS. I don't know as much about it as I want to, and I certainly don't know enough about what therapies are available. It can't be the end of the line because, as I said earlier, all the time there are avenues yet to be explored, there is still hope …

I NEVER PROMISED YOU A ROSE GARDEN

Catherine Mills

For my friend, Janet

As long as you are suffering a burden and try to escape it, things will go badly ...
but if you accept that suffering is what you have to face, then you will know peace.
Thomas a Kempis

I decided to write my story following attendance at a support group for relatives of, and people with, Tourette Syndrome. It is something I have often considered, but never had the confidence to undertake. My mind was finally made up while listening to the problems and experiences of parents of children with Tourettes. I felt strongly that if I had an experience to share, then it was my responsibility to do so. If just one person can draw some strength from my story, then it will have been a worthwhile exercise.

I began writing during February 1998, at a time when I was emerging from a very deep and prolonged period of depression, and it struck me that the process could also hold a therapeutic value. The purpose of relating my story is to try and provide a resource for sufferers from, and relatives or carers of people with TS. It is also my hope that anyone who has suffered from depression may draw some strength from my own experiences. It is very difficult to make sense of what is happening to your body and mind when you are experiencing depression, and all I can say is that I understand. Depression is a terribly lonely state of existence and is something that can only be truly experienced rather than explained. In fact, whilst I have made attempts to explicitly convey the manifestations of TS, I have left the issue of depression more implicit. Perhaps this reflects the fact that I am still too immersed in that state of being, to clearly articulate depression as a clinical state.

I hope that any sufferers, friends, professionals, or other interested parties who read my story may come away with something which will help in the role they undertake. I have found the experience of writing to be a rewarding one, and it has helped me lay a few ghosts to rest. I have recently developed a philosophy whereby I believe we have the opportunity to develop as a person throughout every interaction of our life. We touch each other's lives constantly and I hope this story will make contact with you in some small way, and that you, in turn, will feel able to communicate this to other people.

~

I was initially diagnosed as having Tourette Syndrome in November 1996 at the age of thirty-four, although I have suffered from the disorder since the age of nine. This diagnosis was subsequently accompanied by that of Clinical Depression and Obsessive Compulsive Disorder.

Tourette Syndrome is a neurological disorder characterised by sudden rapid, involuntary movements called tics, which occur repeatedly. Symptoms can include bouts of motor and vocal tics and the focus of these tics tends to wax and wane over time. Typically, tics increase as a result of stress or tension, and may decrease when relaxed or absorbed in a task. However, symptoms are an individual phenomenon, with people exhibiting many different symptoms, perhaps over the course of their own lifetime. Tics are experienced as an irresistible urge (as, for example, in a sneeze), and must eventually be expressed. Many people, including myself, try and suppress their tics until they can find a secluded spot in which to release them. Even then, the feeling of relief tends to be only momentary in nature.

Two categories of tic have been identified, namely simple and complex tics. The simple type includes eye blinking, head and limb jerking; shoulder shrugging and facial grimacing (motor tics), plus sniffing, grunting, throat clearing and yelping (vocal tics). Complex motor tics include jumping, smelling, touching rituals and self-injurious behaviour. Coprolalia (vocalising offensive words and phrases) and Echolalia (repeating a sound, word or phrase just heard) constitute complex vocal tics. Essentially, the range of tics, or tic-like symptoms, which characterises Tourettes, is very broad, and they exist in different combinations. Related problems include (OCD) and hyperactivity, with or without Attention Deficit Disorder (ADD).

Obsessive Compulsive Disorder can take many forms, but most commonly consists of repetitive thoughts and/or actions. The dividing line between normal and abnormal obsessions is often vague, although it can generally be said that someone has OCD if the problem has reached the stage where it is interfering with the quality of their life. Characteristic of TS is ritualistic behaviour whereby everything needs to be evened up, such as touching an object so many times in a certain way. A person may also ask someone to repeat a sentence until it sounds right. Ultimately, OCD may result in behavioural, physiological, cognitive and mood disorders.

Attention Deficit Disorder may occur in children prior to the onset of any other symptoms and indications include poor concentration, being easily distracted, not listening, constantly shifting from one activity to another, general fidgeting and behavioural difficulties. Adults may also exhibit signs of ADHD such as impulsive behaviour, concentration difficulties, learning disabilities and sleep disturbance.

In terms of causation, genetic studies show that TS is inherited as a dominant gene, or genes, there being a fifty per cent risk of transmitting the gene with each separate pregnancy. Gender also influences the expression of the gene, with the incidence of Tourettes being at least three to four times greater in males than in females. However, only ten per cent of people with Tourettes actually experience symptoms severe enough to require medical attention. To my knowledge, there is no one else (thankfully) within my family who has, or has had, Tourettes, other than myself. The gene defect is believed to cause an abnormal metabolism of neurotransmitters, most notably dopamine, within the nervous system and as yet there is no known cure for the disorder. Current research however, is aimed at identifying and understanding how the disorder is transmitted from one generation to the next and the Tourette Syndrome (UK) Association is supporting genetic research into the condition.

I take a medication regime of Sulpiride for my tics and Fluvoxamine for my depression and OCD. I have also received some, and am awaiting further, cognitive therapy for my OCD, although as yet there is no improvement in this condition. The Sulpiride, however, has helped dampen the intensity of my motor and vocal tics and this has helped enhance the quality of my life. The following account explains how my TS symptoms manifest themselves, and some of the difficulties they create in terms of everyday functioning.

Specific areas of my body go into a jerking, twitching, tic-like state, either independently or, more commonly, in a sequential pattern. At its worst, it spreads quickly throughout my body, that is, within seconds or minutes. I am never without the urge to make a movement, and sometimes my body jerks as a whole. The time span of the movements varies in so far as they may be very severe for a few minutes, then settle a little; or more commonly, continue for several hours.

The physical and mental symptoms co-exist, with my concentration and ability to do mental tasks affected. It's like a continual and exhausting interference. Reading is one of the greatest and most frustrating problems, with my mind never being clear of extraneous words or images. Most movements have always been with me, whilst others have come and gone. For example, a particular facial movement may just start, stay for a matter of weeks or months, and then recede. It may at some point return.

I have learned to exert control over the physical movements to the extent that I am able to suppress or disguise them for periods of time, such as when I drive, or am with people. The latter is very tiring, and the longer I suppress them, the more the pressure builds up, and the worse it is when I do let go. When the movements do eventually come out, it is not a pleasant experience and it provides only a kind of temporary, unfulfilled relief.

There are times though when I lose control, such as in shops, or walking along the road, both of which I find stressful.

I have also developed ways of compensating, when it is not feasible to move a certain area of my body. For example, due to additional problems of chronic pain (following back surgery in 1986), it would be very painful if my spine were to move suddenly, so I try and direct the movements to other areas, although there is no part of my body that is not affected. My wrists, elbows, shoulders, legs, ankles, toes, abdomen are all involved. I try and stretch rather than jerk my neck due to the spinal problems, and my mouth, teeth, jaw, nose (including sniffing and smelling) and eyes are all affected. I have experienced injuries in the past, or sometimes an area just becomes painful through continuous, abnormal movement.

Tics are with me from the moment I wake, and they intensify in stressful situations, however slight. When I use the affected part, for example my arm, it starts jerking if I start to write, or use the phone; my teeth and jaws begin grinding or jerking when I brush my teeth. I make a lot of sounds, which vary from meaningless noises such as grunting sounds from my throat or nose, to the repeating of words and phrases out loud. I constantly repeat other people's words and sentences in my mind (Echolalia), usually changing punctuation and putting emphasis on different words. I tend to inwardly 'say' the words, rather than simply 'think' them and also visualise the words in my mind. I *must* complete these exercises, and they preoccupy my mind until I have completed them.

I repeat numbers, always between one and ten, and especially one to five. This sometimes happens out loud, such as when I count my steps along the road. Other sounds, such as a song or tune, will torment me for days and I have to repeat them in different ways. Often I try and replace the words, which torment me, with other words or phrases – such as telling myself to relax – but these then just repeat themselves.

Visually, I line objects up, imaginary or real, and have to move them so that their edges do not touch. I need to keep looking at certain objects in a repetitive way. It is difficult to describe this habit, but again, I *must* do it. I also have a constant stream of unpleasant images. They may be things I have seen on TV, or in a book. Many are to do with blood entering or leaving my body, mutilation, and wounds being opened up in myself or other people. They may involve me swallowing imaginary things and I will actually need to make a swallowing action. The words and images are frequently offensive and distressing (including Copropalia). Some are transitory, whilst other images and words have been with me for many years. Some of the images have their origin in real life experiences, and unlike the physical symptoms, I have no control over them.

I need to perform strange, complex touching movements such as flicking my fingers, tapping the ground, having to repeatedly touch objects, sometimes with my hands, sometimes with other parts of my body. It is extremely difficult for me to keep still and stop myself from undertaking these rituals. Things must also be evened up so that they are symmetrical.

I display extreme obsessional behaviour, which I try to hide or disguise. For example, tasks such as housework must be done in a certain way, at a certain time, follow a particular pattern, and then be checked. Further examples include obsessions around washing and hygiene, as I fear contamination, and meals, which must be prepared and arranged in a particular way. I must also ensure that I do not run out of anything and therefore have a strong tendency to hoard items. I will check a piece of written work many times, perhaps making minor alterations. I will keep going back to check it for hours, because if I do not, my anxiety levels rise, and my movements intensify. Even once the work, such as a letter, has been completed and posted, I will worry about it and do things like check a copy I might have kept.

I have been seeing a cognitive therapist to help me overcome my OCD, in an attempt to make my life more manageable. Presently, there is no area of my life where obsessive, ritualistic behaviour does not dominate. I also have a need to carry a task out immediately, at work or home, and see it through to the end. Things have to be done there and then, even to the point of exhaustion.

At times I become very restless and agitated, for example when I am watching television, and have a constant need to be doing other things that could quite realistically wait. If I feel stressed, or the movements are severe, I can be up and down every few minutes. The need to do this goes on, despite the exhaustion that accompanies it, and the fact it brings no lasting relief. In the long run, I actually feel a lot worse. I try to control or disguise this problem when in company. I also have urges to do irritating things such as press objects to the point where they break, touch hot things, or stare directly at the sun for example. I try hard to resist doing anything that could cause myself harm, but sometimes the urge becomes overpowering. At any given time, at least two or three of the above symptoms will be occurring, often several together.

Worry has been a long-term problem, which has gradually become worse over the years, although it originally manifested itself early on in my childhood. I worry that I have done something wrong, upset someone, made a mistake, etc. I worry incessantly about forthcoming events and then worry again after the event. I wake up worrying during the night, or after I have had a conversation with someone. I also feel a tremendous burden on other people, whether professional or family, and over the years this has resulted in me isolating myself from people, including friends. It is very hard when you feel you have nothing to contribute to a relationship.

I do not think the severity of the physical movements has become worse, but they were becoming more difficult to hide in public around the time of my illness in 1997. The sounds, words, images, obsessions and touching, etc, were definitely becoming worse.

Over the years, I have developed a number of psychological problems, such as the obsessive behaviour, anxiety, depression and eating problems. A lot of these problems became very severe about twelve years ago and, despite extremely positive and caring intervention on the part of the psychologist I was seeing at that time, it is only now that I realise that I concluded my therapy without having any long term coping strategies in place. My psychologist, Jacqui Nevin, helped me through a very acute stage, and I think it was my awareness of issues, which was lacking. As my current psychologist, Sheila, says, perhaps I was just not ready or able to make a complete recovery at that time.

Presently, I am experiencing the benefits of Sulpiride treatment in terms of some of my tics. Some remain in earnest, whilst the constant urge to perform other motor and vocal tics have lessened somewhat and it has become easier to suppress them. My mental images, words, Echolalia and Coprolalia have not responded to any treatment, but I can at least rest in the knowledge that they are not generally visible symptoms, as I still feel very embarrassed about my TS (although I am not saying this is an appropriate feeling). There is also a debate to be considered around the suppression of symptoms. For example, I strongly suppress my motor and vocal tics when in company, but I do not know whether this is actually helpful, as it may literally be storing the problem up and creating an inner tension. There is much to be understood about TS and much awareness-raising needs to be undertaken if children and adults alike are going to have their needs met appropriately and adequately throughout their lives.

~

My earliest memories date back to the age of two or three, when I first recall feeling responsible for the well-being of other people. I would somehow feel I was to blame if everyone in the world was not well and I remember this particularly in relation to my mother, whom I love enormously. It was quite a load for a young child to carry around, and it is only recently within therapy that I have become aware of just how strong these childhood feelings were. Throughout my early childhood I experienced health problems and my school attendance was consequently chequered. When I was at school my concentration was never particularly good and this may have been the first indication that I had Tourettes. My schooling was very strict and was undertaken at the local Catholic preparatory school. I have mixed memories of this period of my life, as, although I enjoyed extensive travel with the excellent choir to which I belonged, I didn't always enjoy the most sympathetic approach towards my academic shortcomings. There was one particular teacher, who, when I was nine, helped mould me into a very nervous, anxious child. It was also around this time that my tics began, although they were probably just interpreted as 'nervous tics' and not associated with any serious, underlying condition.

Around the age of nine and ten, I recall having to blink my eyes continuously, twitch my limbs and make grunting sounds. I could not help these tics, although I used to be asked to stop doing them and sit still. It was a tremendously stressful period of my life, compounded by the fact that I never quite seemed to fit in among my peers. I used to dread going to parties and recall being ostracised during a trip with the choir to Switzerland. There was one teacher who was more sensitive to my needs and tried to help me academically as well as personally, although no one had probably heard of Tourette Syndrome, let alone be in a position to identify it. Unfortunately, my problems were compounded by the fact that I went through an early puberty, and this served to further set me apart from my peers. It was very difficult for me as a child of ten to deal with all these changes occurring in my body at the same time as having to manage the double blow of the onset of Tourettes.

Not surprisingly, I failed my Eleven Plus and then the entrance examination to the grammar school, and was the only child who would not be progressing to the grammar school. I also broke a family tradition, although my parents never imposed any kind of pressure on me. I suppose all these factors just served to contribute to the feeling of being different; a feeling I have carried with me throughout my life.

I was ridiculed at school for being different and became an increasingly anxious child who would worry obsessively about this. It was therefore with a mixture of relief and trepidation that I started a new life at the local secondary modern school in 1973, although, as I was to learn, this was going to be no picnic. Soon after I started at St Bede's, the headmistress of the grammar school telephoned my parents to offer me a fee-paying place at the grammar school. Although I have never previously told anyone, I turned the place down because I could not bear the thought of returning to the prospect of being ridiculed by the same people who had done so at prep school. The only good thing I had to hold on to, was the love of my parents.

At secondary school my confidence and self-esteem plummeted further as my Tourettes developed. Before long I was experiencing severe head, limb and facial jerking as well as the vocal tics. I also began experiencing a constant stream of unpleasant and distressing images and words, which interfered greatly with my concentration and schoolwork. I was put into a low academic stream at school and whilst my images and words were not externalised, they were a continual source of interference and distress. I had one close friend, Elizabeth, and we remain best friends today, but I used to try and hide my bizarre symptoms even when with her.

I developed complex touching movements involving different parts of my body, and would have to perform tasks in a certain way. Apart from my obsessive worrying, I did not start exhibiting obsessional behaviour as such until I was about fifteen, and then it was with regard to studying. I was heavily ridiculed at school and I can recall my movements being mimicked and mocked. People would jerk their heads or make grunting sounds and I am sure it was the memory of this type of experience which eventually led me to disguising my symptoms so well.

Prior to starting my CSE and O Level syllabi, one of my teachers began to encourage me, and my academic performance improved. Soon, other teachers were to start giving me extra tuition and I responded positively to their intervention. I was also given a lot of encouragement in athletics and went on to represent Liverpool in discus throwing. This was one of the few activities I could undertake without serious interference from my Tourettes. I could have gone on to compete in national trials but turned the opportunity down as I lacked the confidence to believe I was good enough. Sometimes I think I have an inbuilt fear of success as this theme has recurred many times during my life. When your self-esteem is being knocked almost every minute of the day, it becomes very difficult to truly believe in yourself.

As a teenager, I was also to experience my first taste of depression and I recall feeling very lonely and low around the age of fifteen. These feelings coincided with my sister Anne's illness, and I know mum was under pressure both with worry and the practical responsibility of looking after her two young children. Everyone was under pressure and I remember one occasion when I involuntarily vocalised an obscenity. I was pinned against a wall by a member of my family and shouted at for uttering such a disgraceful expression. I did not understand what was going on. It was not as though I wanted to say or think these thoughts, but I was in disgrace that night and was desperate that mum would not be told about the incident.

I found studying for my CSEs and O Levels very stressful, as by this time I was experiencing a barrage of torturing mental images, counting rituals, touching rituals, Echolalia, Coprolalia and severe motor and vocal tics. I would compensate for my lack of concentration by studying to the point of obsession. Although I passively accepted that this was the way things had to be, I did sometimes wonder why I had all these strange rituals and habits. But I had never known anything different. This obsession with studying was to heighten when it came to my A Levels, and although I was ultimately to gain five CSEs, ten O Levels and two A Levels, my grades were disappointing, given the amount of studying I undertook. However, just trying to sit still and concentrate within the context of an examination was a challenge in itself.

At the age of seventeen I decided that I wanted to train as a nurse, and therefore applied to my local school of nursing (Sefton) where I began training in September 1980.

1980 – 1986

Having come from a somewhat sheltered upbringing, I found the whole concept of living away from home (albeit locally) and embarking upon a working life, quite daunting. My initial memory of my new life goes back to the first morning of pre-training school, when all the other resident student nurses made their way from the nurses' home to the school of nursing without me. This is just a further illustration of how I did not naturally seem to fit in anywhere, and whilst I did go on to make some friends, there were so many occasions when I would overhear people talking about me in a mocking way. Whilst I was too shy to ever challenge anyone about this, I do not think it was necessarily due to my Tourettes, but rather the fact I was just somehow different. I have certainly always lived in fear of being rejected, and my worst fears were now being realised. I was very unhappy in my nursing at first, and even during my initial ward placement, I was never really accepted as part of the team. However, as my three years of training progressed, I did gain in confidence.

In terms of my Tourettes, things progressed from bad to worse and I do not really know how I managed at times. I was largely unable to control my tics when actually working and, looking back, I know people must have observed them. I would deploy strategies such as hiding in the linen cupboard or treatment room for a few moments, or develop a cough in order to disguise my vocal tics. Dexterous procedures such as dressings and sutures were extremely difficult to master due to my constant need to tic and this became quite damaging to my self-confidence and esteem. I used to think I was making a mess of everything, although looking back, I think I used to compensate by the fact that I was meticulous in all I did. I was certainly slow at some tasks, particularly because of my tics and mental images, and partly because I needed to be so thorough in everything I undertook.

During the second year of my training I became very depressed, but I did not know why. Perhaps, in hindsight, these depressive periods were linked simply with having to cope with Tourettes on a day-by-day, moment-by-moment basis. Perhaps they were biochemically linked with the Tourettes, I am really not sure. I was referred to a psychiatrist and psychologist in order to address my difficulties with depression. Around this time, I did try and tell my GP about my 'twitching', but I was simply prescribed a sedative to be taken when I felt anxious.

I successfully completed my nurse's training in September 1983, and despite the difficulties I had, the last two years of my training were probably the happiest and most carefree years I have experienced. I loved my nursing and feel privileged to have nursed people through sickness, health and death. I have many happy memories and it will be a period of my life that I will always treasure. Unfortunately, none of my student group went on to gain staff nurse posts with Sefton, hence we all departed upon our separate paths through life and things were never going to be quite the same ever again.

My first staff nurse post was on an Orthopaedic Unit at South Shore Hospital, Blackpool. It was a difficult time since the unit had a completely different culture from that with which I was familiar. It was not a training unit; all the staff were considerably older than myself and had been there many years. Initially, they were not too keen on having an out-of-town, newly qualified staff nurse as their colleague, and it was difficult to break through and belong to the team. I very much missed the atmosphere of the training hospital and the friends I had made there.

My introduction to life in Blackpool was helped by the fact that there was another new staff nurse on a different ward, who had come from a similar training hospital background to myself. We later went on to share a flat together and, within the constraints of my Tourettes, life generally improved, both at work and socially. In fact, I was quite happy when, after about eight months, I was offered a secondment to undertake post-registration orthopaedic training at Wrightington Hospital. This would involve me working and studying at Wrightington for a year, subsequent to which I would return to Blackpool. It was an opportunity too good to miss, although in hindsight, it proved to be one of the biggest mistakes of my life. As the saying goes, if it ain't broken, don't fix it.

I commenced my orthopaedic training in July 1984, along with another secondee from Blackpool Victoria Hospital and four other people from the North West. I recall leaving Blackpool for the final time and crying all the way to Liverpool as, despite my initial unhappiness, I had come to value the happier times, which I had enjoyed there. In contrast, I disliked every moment of my time at Wrightington and before my year was through, I was to become seriously ill with Anorexia Nervosa. I lacked control in my life and, along with other course members, was given an ill-defined role at work. On the one hand we were qualified and experienced staff in our own right, and yet we were also students, and treated as such. It was such an ambiguous role to occupy, especially when there were so many things to be observed that you might ordinarily have done differently. I also found it difficult to undertake practical experience across different hospitals in the region, and was generally struggling to control my tics, especially the more anxious and unsettled I became.

In order to try and gain some control over my life, I began to control my food intake and this developed into an absolute obsession. Furthermore, the need to exert control extended into an issue of punishment, and I would use food deprivation as a means of achieving this. Aside from denying myself basic nourishment, some of my food rituals included: constantly weighing food, meticulously counting calories, using low calorie substitutes to an extreme degree (this actually allowed me to eat more, hence reinforce my belief that I did not have a problem), weighing myself many times a day; saving my calorie allowance until late in the day, or carrying it over into the next day, even though it would never be used, always eating the same food products, exercising at every opportunity in order to work off the calories and always preferring to eat in private.

Some of this obsessional behaviour remains with me to some extent even today, and I do not really believe that one ever completely recovers from anorexia. In this respect, it is akin to alcohol dependency. I guess the difference today is that I have an insight to my problem and am able to acknowledge it as such. At the time, I was in complete denial and the further my weight dropped, the less aware I became of the problem. I would also become very irritated if anyone commented on my weight loss and certainly did not feel very good about my gaunt body image or myself. But I was powerless to do anything about it.

I successfully completed my orthopaedic training and returned to my post in Blackpool. However, things had changed. My flatmate had moved on and I subsequently rented a shared flat owned by some good friends of my parents. The flat was pleasant enough, but unfortunately the company was not, and I was very unhappy. More significantly, perhaps, was the fact that I had changed enormously as a person. I was basically very ill. In October that year a more senior post became vacant on the Orthopaedic and Trauma Unit at Victoria Hospital, Blackpool, and I was offered the post. Although it was a teaching unit and I had the advantage of working with my co-secondee from Wrightington days, I think all I was trying to do was to change my external environment in an attempt to compensate for my inner unhappiness.

My eating problems went from bad to worse and as a naturally well built, five foot nine adult, I soon resembled a walking skeleton. Unfortunately, with anorexia, if you consume say 1000 calories one day, then the challenge is to manage on 950 calories the next day, and so on. My weight fell from an initial twelve and a half stone to under seven stone in a little over twelve months. I was subsequently to learn from my psychologist, Sheila, that the rate of weight loss is as significant as the amount of weight loss. Furthermore, it is not possible, in a cognitive sense, to gain an insight into one's condition before one's weight has risen to a certain, individually defined level. I was actually seeing a psychologist, Jacqui at the time, both for my eating disorder and my depression. Sadly, I lacked sufficient insight to make any progress and could see no light at the end of a very bleak tunnel.

My difficulties were compounded by the problems at work that besieged me. Soon after starting at Victoria Hospital, the most horrendous political storm blew up, culminating in the suspension of one, and long-term sickness of another, ward manager. This effectively left me in charge of a large, under-staffed trauma ward, where standards were rapidly declining due to the unmanageable workload. It is difficult and painful to put into words just how awful things were for staff and patients alike. Without question, people received a grossly sub-standard level of care and the memories haunt me to this day. Elderly people were undergoing major surgery without adequate preparation, or after-care, and many suffered post-operative complications as a result. A basic example is that many people were unable to feed themselves and although their meals would eventually be distributed, there were no nurses available to feed them. Consequently, a patient's standard of nutrition would fall, individuals would become prone to pressure sores, infections, etc and their recovery was either delayed, or they died.

Without entering into serious allegations, I believe the hospital's senior management must accept some responsibility. On one occasion my future was even 'secured' on the understanding that I made certain complaints against the two ward sisters who were apparently being scapegoated. Thankfully, I am not a person who can be bought, and despite my many shortcomings, I do uphold certain principles such as loyalty and commitment. On a day-to-day basis, however, it was I who felt responsible for the declining standards. Meanwhile, my own health was deteriorating rapidly, but despite attempts by family and friends to talk to me, I just could not see that I had a health problem at all.

By October, I was barely eating and this behaviour was reinforced by the fact that patients were not being nourished. How could I possibly walk away and eat food when those whose welfare I was responsible for were being deprived of such a basic commodity? I somehow needed to control and punish myself, and food was the means of achieving this. So I continued to work all the hours God sent and yet all I could see around me was total and absolute failure. There were men and women, teenagers and adults all mixed on a ward, which must have been appalling for them.

I started to spend as much of my free time as possible with my parents in

Liverpool and deep down I was very homesick. Upon returning to Blackpool one Sunday evening in November, I experienced a very severe bout of tics and my whole body was jerking all over the room. This was becoming a common occurrence, and on this occasion I severely damaged ligaments in my knee. I went into work the following morning and one of the doctors treated me and sent me home sick. Whilst I was in part devastated at this because of my responsibilities, another part of me was relieved, as it meant I could go home to my parents for a few weeks. My knee was badly injured and, as with other injuries, I had to make up a story as to how it was sustained. The situation on the ward remained desperate. I even received a telephone call one day from the Occupational Health department, telling me not to return to work until my knee had properly recovered. I believe there was a hidden agenda in this message.

I did return to work, but by this time I could barely walk without feeling exhausted. I recall one day walking into a side room where there was a dying, semi-comatose patient and just breaking down in tears. Although it may sound pathetic, I begged her for help, as I somehow felt she would be nearer to God than I. On another occasion, I was attending to a patient who had been slightly incontinent and, to my shame, I did not wash her and change her bed, as I should have done. Having spent my entire career upholding the highest standards, I felt full of shame at my actions, but was utterly and totally exhausted. I did eventually return and attend to the lady in question, but I have never neglected anyone like that in my life before.

In December 1985 I suffered tonsillitis, and although I went into work, I finally had to telephone the on call nursing officer to ask if I could possibly go home. She came up to the ward and was very kind. She was actually in charge of another unit and could not believe the conditions we were working under. I remember vividly her phoning around the hospital and calling upon staff to come and work on my ward for the shift. None of the staff knew the patients, so I gave them the most thorough handover imaginable and then finally left the ward to return to Liverpool. Although I was not to know it at the time, it was the final day of nursing I was every to undertake.

I returned home to Liverpool in December 1985 in a state of total exhaustion. Every attempt was made to try and feed me, but by this time food, as with many other things, had become a total obsession. I initially lay in bed day after day, too ill to move, and really wasn't aware of what was going on around me, or inside me. Following the Christmas period, I started to venture outside a little, but I was very self-conscious, as no one recognised me any more. Rather than take sick leave, I resigned my post at Victoria Hospital, as I knew I could never bear to return to the scene of events I had left behind. Unfortunately I was too ill to attend my psychology appointments with Jacqui, but I told her I was OK; I think this is what I still half believed.

By February 1986, I had decided to apply for health visitor training in Liverpool. I wrote to every health authority for a secondment opportunity, and to the university for a place starting in September. By this time I naively believed I was on the road to recovery and could not see that I still resembled a skeleton. I even started working voluntarily with the Chest, Heart and Stroke Association. I also learned all there was to learn about health visiting and was eventually awarded a secondment by Liverpool Health Authority and passed the university examination. So desperate was I to undertake my health visitor training that I even offered to self-finance my course, and my parents offered to keep me, rent-free! I was therefore devastated when I was called to the university to be informed that they were not going to offer me a place on account of my health. It was put to me that I had anorexia, and perhaps for the first time ever, I realised I had a problem. The tutors were very kind and sympathetic towards my situation, but it was as though my whole future was disintegrating before me. The spring months progressed and I believed I was coming through the worst, although in reality I couldn't have been more wrong.

In May the same year, I obtained a practice nurse post, but just prior to accepting it, I was struck by the most excruciating pain imaginable. My tics became extremely painful, since the slightest movement exacerbated the severe back and sciatic pain I was experiencing. I somehow managed to get into bed and was to remain there for the next two and a half months.

Running concurrently were all my obsessive behaviours and rituals around food and hygiene, to name but two examples. My parents had to look after me and there was obviously a lot of tension around. Living with an anorexic alone is enough to drive some families into crisis, whilst mine had to cope with my myriad of problems. My sister, Mary, would come and see me and help with practical tasks, as I was so physically incapacitated. Perhaps the greatest tragedy, and one that may have contributed to the chronic nerve damage I suffer from, is the fact that I was not altogether believed about my pain. My GP said there was nothing wrong with me other than the muscle spasm, and even my mum wondered (somewhat understandably) if I was using it as an excuse to hide myself away from people. But I wasn't, and went through week after week of agony. I was terrified of having to go into hospital, and again went into a form of denial that there was anything wrong with me that would not get better spontaneously. The thought of going into hospital and having to hide my tics was unbearable, and then there was the whole issue of how I would control my food intake and other rituals.

Eventually I saw another GP who was horrified by my condition, and within a matter of days, I was admitted to hospital and operated on by a neurosurgeon. During my first post-operative night I became extremely ill and was drifting in and out of consciousness. At the time I was afraid of dying, and all I knew was that I wanted to fight back. Despite the fact that death no longer holds such fears for me, I have never taken life for granted since that night.

Despite enormous relief following surgery, there had been a lot of damage to my sciatic nerve, hence I have never been able to resume a fully active life and have gradually had to come to terms with chronic pain. This has caused difficulties in terms of my Tourettes, since any spinal movement is quite painful, especially sudden, jerking type movements.

Meanwhile, tensions were mounting at home due to my very controlled eating rituals. I recall one Sunday when I was on weekend leave from the hospital, being particularly tense. My parents were at their wits' end and I was enormously grateful for my brother Charles' intervention. Not only did he intervene on my behalf, but he also contacted my psychologist, Jacqui, and arrangements were made for her to visit me when I returned to the ward the following Monday. By this time I was profoundly depressed and was helped through this very acute stage by Jacqui's personal and professional intervention. Whilst my most recent depression could be described as a relapse, this in no way reflects upon Jacqui's work with me, but rather the fact I was perhaps not able or ready to fully recover at that time.

I continued to make slow but steady progress through the winter months and gradually put on a little weight, albeit in a very controlled manner. I started going swimming to build up my stamina and I think this helped with my weight gain. By spring 1987, I felt ready to start looking for work again, although I was clearly restricted in what I could manage. I was qualified only for nursing and yet I was not physically able to return to hospital nursing. Even clinic work would have been too heavy and would have necessitated a lot of standing, which was one of the most difficult things to do. I had started to do some voluntary work at Charles' school, working alongside the school nurse, so I put some thought to working in this field. I eventually applied for school nurse posts, most of which existed in the south and in the private sector. I was subsequently offered posts in Surrey, Oxford and Kent, but deep down I was soon to realise I did not want to leave Liverpool.

Apart from wanting to stay personally, my mum's health was not getting any better, having been diagnosed with Parkinson's disease in 1982. I therefore applied for, and was accepted onto a government sponsored community programme scheme in September 1987. This was a temporary post, and apart from lacking somewhat in confidence, I enjoyed my time working in a supervisory capacity on community care schemes.

I secured a permanent post with The Children's Society in 1988 and it was around this time that I decided to buy my own house in order to provide some long-term security. Life with Tourettes basically went on, and in 1990 I applied for a management post with a local voluntary organisation, PSS. My post with PSS certainly held its challenges, as I inherited a poorly disciplined project where standards left a lot to be desired. The service provided supported living opportunities for people with learning difficulties, and was staffed on a twenty-four-hour basis. As with any residential service, it was difficult to keep abreast of events that occurred around the clock, across disparate locations, and it took a number of years to resolve the problems which were being unearthed. The first five years were spent just trying to amend the slack culture that had been there since the project's early days, and there were a lot of disciplinary issues to address.

Such stressful events exacerbated my TS symptoms. I was fortunate in so far as I worked in a small satellite office and shared a room with a wonderful colleague, Chris. I spent a lot of time in the bathroom, or the corridor, if there was no one around, trying to release my tics. Due to the waxing and waning nature of the condition, respective symptoms would trouble me to different degrees according to what was bad at the time. Recurrent problems included keeping my legs still, or trying to use the telephone without making repetitive arm extension movements. Concentration remained troublesome due to the Echolalia and images, etc and I would compensate by working flat out. This served only to reinforce my obsessions around checking work. It is actually very difficult not to continuously check when you know you have not been able to concentrate properly on a task.

My obsessional behaviour became worse upon commencing my Master of Business Administration (MBA) degree in 1992. This was a three-year part-time degree and I found it immensely difficult to keep still and control my tics within the class situation. I also struggled with weekly case studies if we were not issued with them in advance of the class. It was beyond my capability to sit still, clear my mind, read and absorb a case study in class, so I used to try and find out beforehand what case we would be studying and read it many times in advance. Fortunately, there were no examinations (apart from one oral examination linked with the final dissertation) and this was a major factor in me choosing this particular course. Going to the library was a problem, since I became particularly conscious of my motor and vocal tics when faced with quiet surroundings. I also became obsessional about my coursework and would need to start my written assignments as soon as each ten-week module commenced.

The final year was particularly stressful, and I spent every waking moment worrying about whether my work was good enough. Apart from these difficulties, I thoroughly enjoyed doing my MBA! Perhaps my proudest moment ever came on graduation day and I shall never forget just how proud my parents were. Do not misunderstand me, they have never put any pressure upon me to succeed academically, but having done so, they were just so happy to share in my achievement.

In June 1994 I was involved in a road accident and I spent the following eighteen months receiving various treatments for my exacerbated back sciatic pain. In the end, I attended a four-week pain management programme, as I finally had to accept that my pain was not going to return to its pre-accident level. I have to say this was a severe blow.

Having just completed my MBA, a promotion opportunity arose at work and it represented all I had worked for during my time with PSS and throughout my MBA. From the interviews, it ultimately came down to three of us for the two posts that were available. I have never been an over confident person, but I knew I could fulfil the responsibilities of the post in question and it really would have been a dream come true to have gained the post. Unfortunately, I was the third choice candidate, a decision which devastated me. People were very kind and expressed their own views on the matter, and this was a source of consolation to me. But I knew I had done everything right at interview and became extremely anxious because I did not believe I could ever emulate that presentation. I struggled to get over this whole experience, but I have an excellent employer and became determined to make it next time.

Whether triggered by my increased levels of pain, the failed promotion, pressures at work, my Tourettes, general loneliness, or a combination of these and other factors, I do not know, but I started to enter a period of depression during the autumn of 1995. I confided these feelings to my reflexologist, Janet, and she eventually persuaded me to go to my GP. I was received sympathetically and, particularly due to my history of depression, was referred back to the psychiatrist, who prescribed anti-depressants and referred me to a clinical psychologist. Looking back, I think there was just a whole load of stuff inside me that had never come out. Even at this point though, I could not bring myself to tell the psychiatrist about my mental images, words, Echolalia, or motor and vocal tics. In a funny sort of way, I had just accepted that this was the way life had to be.

I started treatment with my psychologist, Sheila, in March 1996, but through no fault of hers I found it very difficult to open up during our sessions. During the summer I was admitted to hospital for a minor procedure and recall lying on my bed crying inconsolably. Apart from mum and dad, I did not receive any visitors and this served to exacerbate my feelings of low self-esteem and unworthiness. I was also finding it difficult to hide my tics in public and my obsessive-compulsive behaviour was becoming worse. I basically felt very different.

My depression worsened during that summer and then one day I found an article at work about Tourette Syndrome. I took it home and read it time and time again and felt sick and frightened as I suddenly realised that this was what I had. I was terrified, as I had never heard of the condition, despite my years of nursing. I plucked up the courage to tell Janet about having movements and thank God she took the matter seriously. I was tremendously embarrassed over my symptoms and Janet spoke with Sheila on my behalf initially. In a funny sort of way, my Tourettes helped break the ice with Sheila and our relationship subsequently went from strength to strength. She was to become a tremendous source of strength to me.

I saw a neurologist, Dr Moore, in the November and he gave me a provisional diagnosis of Tourette Syndrome. I did not find this any source of comfort; in fact it confirmed my worst fears. My depression deepened and I felt as though a life sentence had been passed, especially since no treatment was being suggested until I saw the psychiatrist again. My original psychiatrist had left his post and my new psychiatrist, Dr Agarwal, was not due to take up his post until the new year, so I had to wait a couple of months prior to commencing any treatment.

Throughout the period from about August onwards, my depression became profound. I would go through periods where I would not communicate with my colleagues, or I would gaze at a piece of work, simply unable to cope with it. I would sit there sometimes just crying and the worst time would often be late afternoon, prior to going home to face the evening alone. I was godmother at the christening of my best friend's daughter, but could not face going back to the house afterwards. There were so many basic things that were proving too much to cope with. None of this was helped by the fact that I had to go into hospital twice during the autumn/winter for operations, and face all the accompanying difficulties of trying to hide my Tourettes symptoms. Those winter months were extremely difficult to get through and I owe much to the strength I drew from Janet. In terms of treatment, Dr Agarwal tried different anti-depressants and prescribed Haloperidol for my tics. This medication did not help, and just seemed to make me very drowsy and lethargic. My work performance also suffered and I became increasingly depressed as the spring approached.

Since the disappointment of not gaining promotion in May 1995, I had set my heart on another promotion opportunity becoming available, as indeed it did in March 1997. Two divisional manager posts became vacant at a time when the organisation was undergoing a restructuring and the opportunity was too good to miss. However, deep inside I knew I wasn't well, and secretly wished these posts had become vacant six months or so down the line (although in retrospect this would have made no difference). I was struggling with my medication, in particular the Haloperidol, which was making me feel increasingly depressed and out of control. At the same time, my OCD was increasingly interfering with my work performance and I became obsessed with every aspect of my work. I would do a piece of work and then have to keep checking and re-checking it, often through the night. For example, I would write a letter, then make a series of amendments to it; to the point where I really didn't know what I was writing at all.

Reflecting back on this period, there is no question that Chris was carrying me. I was not only becoming dependent upon her in terms of actually doing the job on a day to day basis, but I needed her company and support during the periods of crying which were becoming a daily occurrence. I would sit at my desk just looking at my work, not knowing what to do and dissolving into the most unbearable, inconsolable bouts of crying. Sometimes this would go on for hours and Chris would sit with me and just be there for me. Throughout this time I would try and put on a cheerful face if anyone was around, but I must have looked pretty awful and certainly was not the greatest company on earth.

The time came to apply for the potential promotion and I tackled the process in my usual meticulous manner, spending time meeting people and finding out what the issues were across different parts of the organisation. I attended for interview on 20 March and presented myself well, although I was somewhat taken aback to be asked about my health and this upset me at the time. However, I received a phone call that evening from the director to ask me to see him the following day. During that meeting, he quite understandably, sought some reassurances regarding my health, and on the exterior I was able to provide them. Deep inside was the most awful feeling of sickness and my obsessive side was in overdrive. But I felt proud to be offered the post of divisional manager on 21 March 1997; it was the fulfilment of a dream. All those years fighting my tics, obsessions, images and depression had brought their reward, and I kept thinking how proud my parents would be.

After my meeting I went to see my good friend and personnel manager, Eileen, and she had bought me a beautiful bunch of flowers. She knew just how important the post was to me and greeted me with a hug. But I was prevented from really enjoying the day due to a constant barrage of anxious and obsessive thoughts. I worried obsessively (and I mean obsessively) about my lack of computer skills, despite the fact that this was not relevant to the post in question. The post involved me moving to head office, and above all, I became fixated upon how I would set about ordering stationery. Rationally, I knew this simply necessitated someone sitting down with me and explaining the system, but I became totally obsessed with the issue and worried about it night and day.

My personnel manager told me about a year later that when I expressed these worries to her, she realised just how ill I was, but initially she tried to reassure me and told me how I would have an induction period during which all these little queries could be resolved, but the obsessive worrying continued and I spent hours crying over it. I was also worried about how I would be able to fulfil my hand-washing rituals, plus various other obsessive characteristics. The whole thing became a living nightmare and this continued over the next few days.

March 24th was my birthday and by this time I was on the verge of total breakdown. My sister, Mary, came to see me and all I could do was cry as I kept staring at a congratulations card which mum and dad had sent me. I knew inside I could not take the post, but I did not want to let my parents down and all I could do was cry.

Despite attempts by my line manager, Rob, to convince me to the contrary, I made arrangements to see my director and let him know I would not be able to take the post. In addition to my own health needs, I did not want to let PSS down, and so it was with a mixture of relief and regret that I relinquished my post before I had even commenced it. One day I sat with Chris pleading for reassurance that no one would make me take the post. I cried and cried and just didn't know what to do. Janet also persuaded me to spend time with Mary and I recall her kindness when she called to see me at Mary's one evening on her way home.

I continued at work until 14 April, at which point I was due for my weekly meeting with Sheila. Within that session I followed what had become a fairly typical pattern, namely being unable to talk due to breaking down in tears. I could simply take no more and was so relieved when Sheila asked me if I wanted to be admitted to the psychiatric ward. I saw the on call psychiatrist and this is when I first started to panic over my obsessions. How would I be able to fulfil all my rituals within the confines of a hospital ward? I knew for my own safety I should go into hospital because I was seriously suicidal and did not trust myself. Eventually, I persuaded the doctor to delay my admission until the following morning, in order to have time at home to attend to my rituals, including preparing clothes, etc for my admission. In return, I agreed to spend some time at my sister's that evening.

The following morning I arrived on the ward and I can only describe it as hell on earth. It was claustrophobic and although I had my own room (upon request due to my Tourettes) I could not bear the atmosphere, or the sparse, dirty, depressing and institutional surroundings. I was mortified at the thought of my parents knowing where I was and God forbid they would ever have to come and see me there. I started to cry and pleaded not to be admitted. The charge nurse kept saying how I needed to be admitted because of my depression, my TS and my OCD and although I knew he was right, he did not understand how strongly I felt about needing to fulfil my rituals. Mary was with me and I was pleading with her to take me home, anywhere but here. During the next three hours the nightmare heightened, and I was threatened with being sectioned under the Mental Health Act if I did not agree to stay voluntarily. I became increasingly agitated and upset and was then told that my 'hysteria' was further evidence of the need to be admitted.

Thankfully, the treatment I received from the charge nurse was the only insensitivity I experienced throughout my care at Fazakerley Hospital. The senior house officer just gently tried to persuade me to stay in and eventually sought counsel from the on call consultant. Mary also contacted Sheila and I don't really know what followed, but eventually I was allowed to go home on the understanding I stayed at my sister's and agreed to meet with a staff member from the day hospital with a view to attending the unit. I willingly agreed to this compromise and would have frankly done anything to free myself from the nightmare of the ward.

The atmosphere at the Oakdale Day Hospital was far less threatening and everyone was extremely helpful and friendly. Here, I met with one of the staff, Marie, a psychiatric nurse. During our initial meeting, she listened to my problems and it helped to release some of the tension from the previous day on the ward. Whilst I did not know it at the time, Marie and I went on to look at my difficulties using a cognitive approach, which helped equip me with practical coping strategies for my depression. However, the priority at the time was staying alive, and a programme was devised whereby I could participate in activities on three days a week, in addition to which I met regularly with Marie and continued my psychology appointments with Sheila. The day hospital became my safe haven and I don't know how I would have managed without it; it was a place where I didn't have to worry if I started to cry and although I felt self conscious, it did not matter if my behaviour did not conform to a certain pattern.

My TS symptoms obviously continued and I was profoundly depressed throughout these summer months, but outside the day hospital, Mary and Janet were wonderful. I found living at Mary's difficult, due to my constant need to tic and the fact I had so many rituals to perform. But I wasn't well enough to carry out everyday tasks such as shopping and cooking, so I used to spend some time at home fulfilling my rituals and then I would go to Mary's.

During the summer, I confided in Charles, and he was to prove a wonderful support, both emotionally and practically; he really looked after me. Meanwhile, other members of my family were given a somewhat modified and sanitised version of my diagnosis. I was embarrassed about what Tourettes entails and, as a private person anyway, I did not like discussing things such as obsessions, tics and depression. Conditions involving the mind are very messy and it is sometimes less complicated to brush matters aside rather than expose oneself to a series of probing questions. I don't necessarily believe this approach is the best, but more often than not, it is the easiest. Above all, I wanted to protect my parents from the horror of my Tourettes and related problems. They worry about me so much and would find it extremely painful if they thought I was experiencing such suffering. With mum and dad I use the analogy of Parkinson's disease, since mum has this condition and can readily relate to it. I have explained that my condition is due to an excess of dopamine, whereas Parkinson's is due to a deficiency of the chemical. They are aware that Tourettes is a genetic condition and mum certainly feels responsible, even though this may not be the case. Even if I have inherited the condition, it can make no difference to a loving relationship, and I have never thought of attributing any blame to either of my parents.

During the summer months I regularly saw Dr Agarwal, and I found him to be an extremely sensitive and pragmatic doctor, whom I could talk to in the knowledge that he was listening. I also saw the day hospital doctor, Dr Sikdar, and was prescribed a variety of medication regimes, which included Clomipramine and Fluvoxamine for depression and OCD, Venlaflaxine for depression and Clonazepam for tics. My Haloperidol was discontinued in the April, as it was thought the drug was contributing to my depression. None of the drugs was proving effective in the slightest, and it was during this time that I requested a consultation with Dr Hugh Rickards at his specialist Tourettes clinic in the Queen Elizabeth Hospital, Birmingham. Dr Agarwal readily agreed to this, although it was 30 September before I was to see him due to the difficulty in securing funds for the extra-contractual referral.

Charles took me to Birmingham where we met with Dr Rickards and his senior registrar. My consultation lasted two and a half hours and for the first time ever I felt some sense of relief, even if only to be given a confirmed diagnosis. In addition to suggesting cognitive therapy for my OCD, Dr Rickards prescribed Sulpiride in place of the Clonazepam I was taking at the time for my tics. Additionally, I was to continue on Fluvoxamine for the depression and OCD. The consultation was one of the most intense experiences of my life and Charles and I came away exhausted, yet satisfied. Just to talk to someone who had expertise about Tourettes was such a relief, and although I could not say I felt a sense of hope, as I was too depressed to experience such an emotion, I could at last make some sense of the bizarre symptoms I had experienced since the age of nine. Finally, someone understood, and I was able to begin the process of coming to terms with my condition.

The next step in the process was to gradually withdraw from

Clonazepam, which belongs to the Benzodiazepine family of drugs. Despite following a careful withdrawal regime, I experienced the most awful side effects. I was literally exhausted and lost my limb sensation to the extent I was often unable to walk. I would shake and have strange twitching movements that were different from my usual tics. The Sulpiride was helping some of my physical symptoms, although it was difficult to enjoy this experience due to the intensity of my withdrawal symptoms. I would also say my depression took a further plunge around this time and the only peace I could find was in my constant suicidal thoughts. I would bathe in the near happiness of these ruminations.

Throughout this period I used to talk to Mary and Charles when I could pluck up the courage to phone, or if they contacted me. They were a tremendous support, as was Janet, who remained an absolute rock throughout. Upon reflection, I felt very lonely at the time, but I still had support from the day hospital and my psychologist, and people at work remained very loyal. It was just that every minute alone was becoming unbearable.

Around this time I started cognitive work with Marie and began to keep a diary, which would form the basis of our discussions. Cognitive therapy is concerned with recognising unhelpful thoughts/cognitions and developing strategies to challenge these. It was used within the context of depression with me initially and, later, to help treat my OCD. The first step is to become aware of one's 'negative automatic thoughts' and the situations that trigger them. Negative automatic thoughts lead to negative feelings about oneself, although initially it can be quite difficult to distinguish those thoughts which are reasonable in a situation, from those which are out of proportion, and therefore unreasonable. Cognitive therapy helps challenge negative thought patterns such as over-generalisations – all-or-nothing thoughts; jumping to inappropriate conclusions; catastrophising; making 'should' statements; personalising issues; and overlooking the positive.

One of the techniques I was taught is termed 'laddering', in which I would record all my negative thoughts, thereby bringing them into the conscious mind. I would record thoughts and experiences that could be described as negative, and with the help of Mary, try and challenge these negative thoughts and identify a more positive approach. This was easier said than done at times!

Meanwhile, I continued my work with Sheila and she would help me to look at underlying issues such as the rules and regulations that govern my life. For example, one of my problems is that I feel responsible for other people's well-being and happiness. If they are not happy or content, then it is in some way my responsibility. We would look at the possible origins of my problems and I found this form of therapy complemented the cognitive work very well.

The winter months were difficult to manage and I even had to give up an evening class I had started in aromatherapy. Once again, I became obsessive over the work and could not leave it alone night or day. It was basically too much pressure and I had to start acknowledging that I had to come off the treadmill and let my body and mind rest. I also began to accept that it was not helpful to keep going into work, albeit informally, and perhaps this kind of acceptance was the first real step on the path to recovery, even if I did not appreciate it at the time.

So the months passed and I remained in a semi-functioning state, not daring to believe I was capable of being liked, or worthy in any way. I carried around these feelings of always letting people down and felt a constant need to apologise for my shortcomings. The onset of depressive periods can be likened to sitting in a dentist's waiting room – you know your name is going to be called, and there is no escape from it. You know it's going to hurt and the soreness will linger for some time afterwards. The metaphor falls down, however, in so far as the depression lasts much longer and there is no anaesthetic to provide relief during the most acute phase. Somehow you just cling on to the ladder, which descends into your pit, even though you do not always feel as though you want to cling on. With me, my motivation for clinging on came from not wanting to let down all the people who were helping me, and not wanting to hurt mum and dad. I could not bear to think of them having to cope with the death of their daughter whom they love so much, and who loves them. When it came to the crunch, this is what kept me alive.

It was cautiously suggested that there was a slight uplift in my mood following the Christmas period, but I did not actually feel any better in myself. The medication was helping my tics, but all I wanted to do was sleep all day long. I was desperately tired and felt weak all the time. Feelings of suicide constantly haunted me and I would have days when I deprived myself of food to a serious degree. I could see no hope and frequently felt frustrated and angry with myself for the way my life was shaping. I felt desperately unhappy and struggled to see any hope of getting back to work either in the short or long term. Meanwhile I met with my employers, and they remained tremendously supportive towards me. Work is a very important part of my life and my ultimate aim was to return successfully – not to the way things were before – but to a new and hopeful beginning. Unfortunately, words such as 'hopeful' were difficult for me to say, let alone comprehend.

I finally woke up on 10 February, having had an awful day previously, and something seemed to have changed from within. It was a very tentative change, but I just could not bear spending another day the way I had been existing. I was determined to somehow claw my way back to the top of the pit and do things differently. I met with Marie that day which encouraged me a lot, and also with Dr Agarwal. Some suggestions were made as to how I could perhaps redistribute my medication regime, which proved helpful in terms of my tiredness and lethargy. I soon went on to deploy strategies such as building in regular rest periods through my day and gradually felt slightly more energised. Somehow that day I knew things had to change, and sooner rather than later.

Gradually, I began to interact better with people at the day hospital and could actually understand the benefits, in terms of support and interaction, of groups such as the art and pottery, and actually learned to laugh a little at my mistakes and myself. Our pottery teacher, Lena, would talk about how we were in control of the clay (although in my case that was debatable!) and, equally, how we were the authors of our own lives. The day hospital gradually shifted from being a safe haven, to becoming a place for development and advancement.

Meanwhile, my diary recordings were reflecting my upturn in mood and I was hungry to build on this. One of the beauties of maintaining a diary is that you have a record of positive events to reflect upon. There have been some not so good days since 10 February, but I now have a record to remind me how you can have good days and positive experiences. It is important to have this in writing, since once you start descending into your pit, it becomes very difficult to simply remind yourself from memory how things can be okay. Such memories easily become very blurred.

I was continuing with my psychology, and looking at issues such as not being responsible for other people's feelings and actions. I also learned how I have always clung on to my 'pillar of certainty', which in my case was my feelings of badness and unworthiness. Sometimes, one just needs a certainty to cling on to, regardless of whether it comprises positive or negative feelings. Gradually I started to let go of my pillar and began to take some tentative risks, including the risk of being rejected by people. Between my work with Marie and Sheila, together with my group activities at the day hospital, I slowly started to build up a repertoire of coping strategies in respect of my depression. I was learning to challenge negative thoughts and beliefs spontaneously, and replace them with more positive alternatives.

Meanwhile, I started making plans for my return to work, my scheduled date of return being 1 April. A number of changes have taken place during my absence, and this presents a great challenge to me for the future, which I face with both excitement and trepidation. In particular, I do not know how I will manage in terms of my OCD, plus the interfering mental symptoms which characterise Tourettes. However, I have tremendous support in the form of my managers and colleagues. One thing I do know is that I have more coping strategies for my depression in place than at any time in my life, which is a source of encouragement.

At the time of concluding my story, I am experiencing no relief from my tortuous words, images, Echolalia, etc, and it is like having to process multiple sources of stimuli at once. However, my physical and vocal tics have improved by some fifty per cent. I still have severe OCD and continue my treatment for this. My depression feels more under control than at any time I can remember, and I feel prepared for the dips that will inevitably confront me in the future.

The future, therefore, holds both fears and expectations. My immediate aim is to manage my depression; an element of which I accept may always remain with me, whether due to biochemical or other factors. I continue to attend psychology sessions, participate in an assertiveness/confidence building group at the day hospital, and await further cognitive therapy in respect of my OCD. The future now holds some structure and hope; expressions which at one time I did not think I would be able to use. I hope to cultivate more outside interests as I gain in confidence and believe that important foundations have been established over the past twelve months in this respect. It is said that you have to hit rock bottom before you can begin to climb again, and I for one, would not argue with this painful reality. But climb you can, and we must always remember; we do not walk alone.

Life with Tourettes and depression is not easy, but after all, no one ever promised us a rose garden.

Acknowledgments

I gratefully acknowledge the support, love and compassion extended to me by so many people during my lifetime. I have been fortunate in that many people have touched my life in such a meaningful way, especially during periods of crisis. Specifically, I would like to thank my parents for their unconditional love and for always being there despite my many shortcomings. Thank you especially to my sister, Mary, and her family, who have so warmly welcomed me into their home, and to my brother, Charles, who has invariably been there when I needed him.

During my most recent period of illness, my employers, PSS, have treated me with the utmost sensitivity and kindness. They have kept faith in me throughout my twelve months' absence and have always been available to provide me with support and encouragement. I do not underestimate the importance of their role in my recovery. Special gratitude is extended to my friend and colleague, Chris, who not only maintained things at work during my absence, but also provided the most wonderful personal support I could have asked for. She protected me from pressure when I was too ill to cope, and involved me gradually as I started to pick up the threads of my life.

Professionally, I feel privileged to have received a quality of service provided by all those involved in my care, and to all, I extend my heartfelt thanks. My facilitator at Fazakerley Oakdale Unit, Marie Reid, and my psychologist, Sheila Hamilton, have supported me enormously throughout my most recent illness, and I will remain eternally grateful for their role in providing me with the strength to carry on. They were always there when I needed them, and their sincerity made it easier to call upon their help.

There is one person who has struggled with me along every step of the journey since 1995, that is my reflexologist, Janet Wilkinson. Without Janet, there is no question that I could not have made it through. She is the first person I confided in about my Tourette Syndrome, and the person who fought stoically to get me into the health care system at that time. Janet has never once let me down, despite the tremendous pressure I have put upon her, and has been a constant factor in my life over the past three years. Janet has given selflessly to me and her hugs kept me going on many an occasion.

There are many other people whom I recall with gratitude and fondness, and in my mind I have not, and will not, forget them. So many people have helped shape my life, and I hope that by sharing my story, I can put something back into the lives of others.

A LIFETIME OF BEWILDERMENT

Ruth Oliver

'When young, her mother protected her from admission to a mental hospital ... Her life has been a constant battle to hide the manifestations of her neurological disorder. She describes this as never having been able to have an unguarded moment. It is difficult to understand how difficult this must have been for her ...'

I was almost sixty years old when I read these words, and words cannot express how I felt when doing so. Certainly unbounded relief, but more a quiet communion with God. I have always known that at some time before I died, God would provide me with the means to understand the sheer bizarreness of my life. The comments above, written by a consultant neurologist, were the first clue I had ever received as to the true nature of my condition. The initial diagnosis of Tourette Syndrome had been made by a young psychologist who used me as a case study, and I shall be eternally grateful for this first indication that I was not a one-off freak, and that I was not alone. My instinctive reaction to this was simple joy, especially when I learned that there are thousands of people all over the world who suffer from TS. Unfortunately, a diagnosis was all there was for me. Drugs are being used now, especially for children, and progress is being made. But with the advice of my consultant, I decided that at my age, the start of a drug programme was not feasible.

The introduction to the man who made such an impact on my life came about through a visit to a GP, but a GP with a difference. She was the first woman doctor I had ever consulted. She chose to send me to a neurologist instead of a psychiatrist, and it was only then, just a few years ago, that my world began to slide into kilter. Tourette Syndrome, and the many problems it has caused me, were fully discussed and gradually my life began to make a little more sense. At last I understood God's reasoning for keeping me here when I had always considered my life to be pointless. My fundamental instinct to commit suicide had always felt like slapping God in the face, and now I am glad that I resisted the urge to do so.

There has been only one occasion when it almost happened, but it was not a serious attempt. It was a simple mistake, but no one believed me. It happened at a high point in my lifelong see-sawing association with depression, and my doctor had given me ten Laudanum tablets, because the many other sleeping pills he had prescribed had been ineffective. I was really not aware of taking an overdose. I was conscious only of wanting to stop, not only the screaming torment that was going on in my head, but also the unceasing and frantic bodily jerks that were sending me crazy. All I wanted to do was sleep, but the handful of pills I scooped up after spilling the contents of the bottle on to the table knocked me out quickly, taken as they were after a good deal of alcohol. I was alone, not expecting anyone for hours, but in the event I was found in time and subsequently recovered. God again – stepping in when He was needed, since the thought of suicide had not even entered my head on that particular night.

Suddenly, with that one diagnosis, my whole life changed and I found that I could be of some use in furthering an understanding of the condition. My brain could be examined after my death with the possibility of answers being found, and I happily agreed to undergo a ninety-minute brain scan to help with research.

I have since pondered on the fact that had I consulted a woman doctor earlier, perhaps my own enlightenment might have been improved. Given the sexually-orientated nature of some of my tics, perhaps only a woman could take on board the terrible stress that they engendered. Perhaps only a woman could understand the overwhelming feelings of physical as well as mental pain, paramount of which is unadulterated shame, caused by the beating of my breasts and pubic area with a relentless fist, hour after hour, day after day; and perhaps it needed the instincts of a woman to realise that I was not just neurotic. The young psychologist who made the initial diagnosis was also a woman.

What are the tics associated with Tourettes? Put simply, they are uncontrollable movements of the body which are embarrassing, futile, and sometimes dangerous. They create a wall between the sufferer and the outside world. Behind that wall, the whole consciousness consists of a raging battle that ceases only when forced into sleep, hence, for me, the sleeping pills. The tics are the first thing that enter the mind on waking, so getting out of bed each morning to face the coming day is another struggle. Every scrap of energy is spent trying to control them in order to get through the daily routine with some semblance of normality, and a constant sense of failure can lead to attacks of aggression and sometimes violence – in my case, towards myself, although violence towards others, and wanton destruction, can be a feature of the illness. This is brought about by frustration and a feeling of helplessness, of being trapped in some sort of nature warp, and in rare cases is expressed in Coprolalia, the shouting out of obscenities, sometimes with such force that the words are literally spat out of the mouth. Mercifully, in my case, this condition, at its worst, lasted only about a year, and somehow, I have lived my life with great hopes for the future. An innate optimism, which I attribute directly to God.

I have spent my entire life looking for ways to hide my 'habits', which is how I thought of them long before I heard the word Tourettes, and I became clever over the years in disguising them within the parameters of normal movements, so that I was able to lead a life that, to others, appeared no different from their own. It is amazing what surreptitious movements can be made under the guise of normal ones, such as dropping things on the floor, tightly gripping such things as umbrellas, or rolled up newspapers, the shifting about of packages, handbags, etc, lifting a handkerchief up and down, gripping the edges of tables or desks, or simply turning away from companions, or a crowd, in order to create a blind side. I use these and many others to hide, while at the same time satisfy, my uncontrollable urges. However, when the use of subterfuge is no longer possible, the only thing to be done is to tense every muscle, hang on, and immediately seek solitude, although wrapping one's arms around the torso and rocking backwards and forwards can help a little.

The movements of TS vary from person to person and they wax and wane. Old ones lie dormant for a long time, then shock you with their reappearance, and new ones will hit you out of the blue. Each one creates its own despair, and a constant cry in the mind of, "Dear God, why am I doing this?" About a year ago I developed a habit I had never done before. On being faced with going through a door (going through doors has always been a particular hell and is associated with Agoraphobia) I suddenly started to jerk downwards at my hips and knees. Trying to squat, in fact, up and down, up and down, in the frenetic, fast and furious tempo that characterises all Tourettes tics. The desperation of trying to stop, coupled with a determination to complete the normal action, creates a screaming point of tension so strong that you feel a seizure is imminent. Sometimes, the thought of that happening is preferable. Imagine trying to control this while trying to go through your own front door, with so many watching windows around you.

Of late, it has begun to affect me while walking along the street, and I continually have to fight the urge to do it. It helps if I walk at a reasonably fast speed. But if I have to slow down, perhaps to avoid bumping into someone, or if I have to pause in order to cross a road, then the urge cannot be appeased by the speed of walking, or by tightening the muscles around my lower spine, or by thumping my heels heavily on the ground, or by a sharp backward jerk of my torso, all performed in miniature so that, hopefully, they will go unnoticed. I could go on and on. However, these miniscule movements can only relieve the situation for so long before panic sets in and you know disgrace is about to descend upon you. That is when you flee, into a room, or any space empty of people where you can let go. On one occasion, when I could no longer hang on, I ran across the road, heedless of the traffic, with my daughter's cry the only external thing I was conscious of, "Mother, look out!"

I was born with TS, although for most of my life I thought it was the result of a traumatic childhood, but maybe my painful childhood was the result of being born with TS. Who knows? Maybe it was a combination of both. Certainly the fact that I come from a background of extreme poverty, where even chronic toothache had to be endured because treatment was out of the question financially, was a major factor in any possibility of help. It just was not there.

Tourette Syndrome is a serious neurological disorder caused by a chemical imbalance in the brain. Little else appears to be known and much research is needed. Understandably, I have sometimes felt a little bitter about a lifetime spent creating painful situations for myself and everyone around me, but this bitterness was never directed at God. For I knew that everyone had a cross to bear and I was not doing a very good job of bearing mine, in the sense that I could not overcome the misery it caused me. This feeling never lasted long because God always reassured me with a shot of optimism which enabled me to carry on. Today I am thankful for what I have, especially my children, and for the things I can do now that have been impossible before.

My earliest memories, from about five, do not include any experience of TS, but maybe I do not remember them. By the time I was seven, however, I was in the throes of the illness. How my parents and my older siblings coped with the incessant and weird habits I had developed by then, I shall never know. I could not cross a room without executing a complete circle three or four times, one after the other, and very fast. I must have looked like a miniature dervish. Blackouts were common and I was frequently, as I learned when older, thought to be dead because I had turned blue. My heart goes out to my mother in her distress, for I know how I would feel in the same situation.

Lamp-posts were another focus. I would always get past them without any problem – this was part of the ritual – but heaven help the person I was with if I was not allowed to go back and touch every one. If I was refused, they had a fighting, screaming banshee on their hands. As I grew older, any action that needed the extension of my arm to its fullest extent was agony. I would stand thrusting it back and forth in bursts of rapid action for what seemed like hours, in an attempt to press a light switch, or post a letter, knock on a door, or pick something up. I would not succeed until my frustration reached boiling point and I would then complete the action with a violence that would leave me with a bruised hand.

Frantic eye movements had started too. A crazy compulsion to turn them a hundred and eighty degrees in their sockets. This was accompanied by all manner of facial tics and jerking of my head, limbs, and torso, and my fingernails were bitten to the quick. I counted incessantly in my head, anything and everything, which made me want to scream aloud, and when I was not doing that, my head was filled with evil thoughts that caused tremendous guilt, especially in church, so I wondered how God could stand it, let alone me. I made clicking noises with my mouth, spitting was common and I grunted from the back of my throat, and painful pressure was inflicted on various parts of my body with fingers that seemed to have a strength kept purely for that purpose.

All these were part of my daily routine and were accompanied by a stultifying anxiety at the thought of moving a single muscle; while panic attacks were so common they seemed to be just another habit. My body was never still, constantly on the move, which was very tiring. Persistent tiredness has always been a notable factor for me when undergoing general physical examination, with vague references to a 'tired heart' echoing through the years. This possibly accounts for the fact that I was fitted with a pacemaker twelve years ago when, over a period of some months, my pulse rate went down to twenty-seven.

As I approached my teens, the banging of my breasts and pubic area started – the one habit that has never left me. Others have come and gone and some have returned, but this particular one just goes on forever. Such was the embarrassment fifty years ago when sex and its organs were taboo, it became the final straw for my family and, where before I had simply been ignored, I was now invisible. Sex, however, has nothing to do with it – there is nothing sexually satisfying in my actions. They are, in fact, very painful, and it was the onset of this habit that caused shame to rear its ugly head. From then on, life began to pass me by completely. After all, puberty is bad enough for everyone, but making a public spectacle of oneself is something else, so that reclusiveness now became part of my life.

Long periods were spent at the window watching other children play, or sitting in corners literally trying to be invisible. I did go to school, however. I had to do that. Had I not done so, someone would have had to confront my problem and I was too scared to allow that to happen. Also, it would have greatly upset my mother whose suffering I watched, and which caused further guilt in me.

Spending long periods alone has always been a factor in my life. I once spent six weeks sitting in a hotel room from seven in the morning to eight in the evening, only creeping out to the library once or twice a week. The whole of each day I simply sat by the window in my room watching golfers on an adjoining course and alternately knitting and reading. What happened to my mind during those days, and at other times that this has happened, I do not know for sure, but I believe that I switched off when left alone and did not switch back on again until I was once more joined by another person.

At this particular time I was over forty years old, but such experiences have been quite common in my very restricted existence. For almost fifteen years before my discovery of TS, I lived in one of the most beautiful areas of the West Country. There were no other buildings in view and the whole setting was idyllic, but it was, nevertheless, a prison. A prison of my own making, maybe, but caused by continuing depressions of varying intensity because TS keeps a sufferer in a stranglehold of helplessness. They were such wasted years.

But going to school was normal, and since the fact that I was abnormal had never been allowed to surface from my subconscious, I really had no choice, and coped with the taunts of my schoolmates as best I could. I had become a listener, too, when sitting quietly, and on one occasion heard myself being discussed; the words 'mental asylum' striking terror into my heart. So before I was ten years old, I began working on disguising my habits, though I do not think this was a conscious decision, more a gut instinct for survival.

My embarrassing movements were turned into seemingly innocuous behaviour, acceptable, though irritating, and my vocal tics into pathetic attempts to sing. In recent years I have come to realise that I have always had a good singing voice, though it is fading fast now, but I do wonder how different my life would have been had I been able to make use of this talent. Even, perhaps, have made a career from it, for, like most people, I have always envied those who are able to earn their living by doing something that gives them pleasure. Nevertheless, now when I sing in church I get a satisfaction that at one time I would have thought impossible. But then I am singing for the One who gave me my voice in the first place, along with the ability to see and hear. He gave me a rich life, despite this story, especially in my children who do not know how much I love them, and in my music, for when I hear piano and orchestra in full concerto, or the human voice at perfect pitch and tone, then I know that God is near.

During those years I became very isolated. I still functioned as best I could as a member of the family but the lowest possible profile was essential. I suppose I made an aloof shadow of myself by persuading myself that if I did not seek out, or expect attention, I would get by. I've no doubt that peer pressure existed then as it does now, but I was not aware of it. Other children did not exactly shy away from me as though I had a contagious disease, but I was not included in group activities and no one made a special chum of me. It was my lot, if I could not persuade my teacher to allow me to stay indoors, to stand at a distance and watch. My sense of worthlessness was so great that I saw nothing unusual in this, and considered every slight and rejection to be my own fault. If I could only get rid of my habits, then, perhaps, people would like me a little more. I felt responsible for my own misery in having to watch other children shout with laughter while they ridiculed my habits by aping them. That was bad enough, but having my arms trapped behind my back by other children and being physically prevented from performing, left me weak and heaving with stress. I do not suppose I was ever trapped for more than a few moments, since my struggles to free myself were extremely violent, but during these struggles, I thought my brain would burst; caused, not by the children's actions, but by my own inexplicable feelings of electrifying terror. Terror of what? I cannot put that into words, but my self-esteem, and my nerves suffered badly.

This readiness to blame myself rather than others was to escalate in later life to rationalising the behaviour of adults with whom I attempted any kind of relationship, even when it was obvious that I should not have done so, when such behaviour made me suffer even more. I can see now that I made it easy for others to dominate and take advantage of me. I think I allowed it because doing so meant that I might be granted some measure of acceptance, and if that meant being bullied, so be it.

It was in my early teens that I came to believe that my life was in some kind of limbo, that it had not really started. It would begin sometime in the future when I would overcome this freakishness that was holding me back, when the world would stop and I would be able to get on! Then I would be able to enjoy a normal, carefree existence. The idea of my life beginning later when things would be different was to stay with me for a long time and I realise now that hope was the key – given to me by God, plus my reliance on Him to put my life in order very soon. One thing I have never done is ask "Why me?" That is God's domain and will always remain so.

Puberty for me was catastrophic. The strain of struggling from childhood to early womanhood was magnified immensely by the fact that, by this time, my right arm was punishing me unmercifully, though I had forced myself to stop biting my nails. Since vanity could not take its normal adolescent form, it nevertheless had to be expressed somehow, and I could at least manage to have nice hands and manners. However, just as my childhood is mostly recalled through the misery of isolation, so my teenage years are a blur of confusion and a continuing pattern of self-effacement.

One notable thing happened that, with different results, might have made a difference. I was entered for the Eleven Plus examination, which meant a chance of going to grammar school. When the results came through my name was not on the list and I took this to mean that I had failed. As it happened, my results were delayed because of a borderline decision, and when I learned that I had been successful, I was completely overwhelmed. I had been silently praying since the moment I had been told I could take the exam. He had listened, and better than that, He had performed a miracle, because there was no way I could have done it alone. Being the youngest of a family of nine and the only one to take the exam, I felt sure that the news would be received at home with approval, if not delight. In the event, I was sent hurtling from cloud nine with harsh words, and was forced to the conclusion that ambition and success were other facets of my odd behaviour. This reinforced my belief that what appeared normal for the rest of the world, was something quite different for me. Ergo, I did not really exist.

On the intervention of a family friend, however, I was allowed to take up the scholarship, but only until I was fourteen. Then I was made to leave because I was old enough to work. I can remember little of my two and a half years at the school, not even the name of a single teacher or pupil, but I have the sense that I enjoyed it, and this, along with my lifelong failure to react in given situations, makes me feel that ADD has also been a symptom of my condition. This would account for my lack of concentration in exams and schoolwork in general.

The lack of reaction to events manifests itself in an inability to show surprise or shock, pleasure or delight, etc, when incidents causing such reactions come without warning. However, when there is the slightest indication that something is about to happen and I know that some reaction is necessary, these reactions often have to be simulated. Then those around me sense that my behaviour is not genuine and slowly remove themselves from my presence. Not physically, necessarily, but by withdrawing their attention from my sphere. Concentration, too, is often difficult, to the extent that sometimes only a few minutes is enough before my mind becomes a blank and I lose the thread of whatever is going on. Impulsiveness, a recognised symptom of TS, is particularly trying, causing a tremendous waste of time, effort and very often money, leaving you with a feeling of having behaved so stupidly you cannot truly believe what you have done. For you know at the time that what you are doing is seriously wrong for you, but it is as if you are pre-programmed, and having got a thought in your head, you can see neither beyond, nor around it, so that warning signals are ignored. It is a sort of psychological tunnel vision.

In retrospect, I believe that had I been allowed to finish my education, my life might have been very different. I believe myself to be of average intelligence and would have achieved more had I been able to concentrate on the learning and development essential to normal growth. TS has stolen the potential for success of any kind which may have been in my character, by denying me the ability to do even the simplest task. Instead, such was my obsession with the business of controlling my habits, my need to work out new ways to hide them, and my determination to stay one step ahead of a strait-jacket, that learning and development had to pierce my psyche as best they could, and I handle my condition by covering up not only my physical aberrations but also my lack of education. This means that I present a false image, which sometimes leads others, on first acquaintance, to imbue me with professional status. I seem to be powerless to prevent this and my skin crawls with embarrassment when the truth finally dawns.

Yet, as a child, I remember an occasion which made such an impact on me that I felt, even then, that I was justified in recognising the potential which I had always felt was within me. I was about nine or ten and taking part in a school project for the writing and delivering of a speech, purporting to come from a city councillor on the advantages of a proposed new road. I worked very hard on the project, and having a naturally good vocabulary, I knew the result was good. I managed to make the speech, enduring the nightmare of standing still in front of the class by hanging on to every muscle with all the strength I could muster, but becoming increasingly bewildered by the look on my teacher's face. However, I managed to go on to answer the questions the class were encouraged to put to me, until my teacher floored me by asking how much the scheme would cost. Too young to realise that such a question needed specialist knowledge and having had, by this time, more than enough, I plucked a nonsense figure out of thin air. Seeing what I thought to be contempt on my teacher's face, I crept back to my seat with my usual sense of paralytic shame.

After the lesson was over, I followed him round, trying desperately to pluck up the courage to ask him what I had done wrong, only to overhear him telling two other teachers about my speech and commenting, "She couldn't have written it herself. I expect her father did". I cannot remember what I felt on hearing this, but it obviously could not have done me any good. Most people suffer setbacks such as these when growing up, but they are able to overcome them as their confidence and self-esteem increases with their progress into adulthood. What they do not have is the crippling knowledge, as TS sufferers do, that everything they do is judged and condemned in the light of their abnormal behaviour, and this puts them, always, in a no-win situation.

The usual teenage interests and pursuits were, in the nature of the creature I had become, denied me. I had no interest in clothes or make-up, and as for boys, the idea was ludicrous. In any case, the surge towards adulthood was exacerbating my condition to the point where I first contemplated suicide. My natural reluctance to do this, however, was encouraged by the thought that God would take me soon, because I could not see how my body, let alone my mind, could go on standing the enormous physical and mental strain. The combination of puberty and TS was too much and I wanted very much to die. But I did not. I think I simply switched off.

From that point in my life, it seems to me that I was wafted along only by the eddies of other people's waves. If it is psychologically possible, I think I became incapable of active thought, as if my brain had simply atrophied. However, I had to work. It is difficult to just refuse to move; especially when the alternative is the mental asylum image of prolonged cold baths and electric shock treatment that I was carrying around in my head.

Getting a job was not often a problem. I was personable enough to look at, being fastidiously neat and clean, and I was articulate. Providing interviews were not too long, I could control myself while they lasted, heading for the nearest loo as soon as they were over to let my arms fly, and anything else that wanted to, in order to breathe easily again. Therefore, the beginning of each venture was satisfactory. But employers could not know that my efforts to make myself indispensable were an attempt to soften the blow of what would soon become apparent. It was inevitable and there was no way I could avoid it. I could delay it with my hiding tactics for as long as I was able, but that was not long at that time in my life.

Gradually, in the familiarity of most working environments, someone would come up behind me, or appear in front of me unexpectedly, or enter a room I was in unnoticed because I was absorbed in what I was doing. They would see 'performances' before I was conscious of anyone being there, and the result was always the same – a flush of colour, or a frozen face, would be followed by a look of incredulity and a quick exit from my presence, and when we met again there was a noticeable change in attitude. Coolness, reserve, a sort of stepping back, often with such embarrassment that even routine conversation became difficult. So I was forced to move from job to job.

Occasionally, as I approached my twenties, I would be aware of male interest, which would make me even more cautious, but to no avail. Either he would see my habits for himself, or I would suspect that he had been told. Either way, my discomfort was profound. However, God's comfort was always there. Without it, picking myself up, dusting myself down, and starting all over again, would have been impossible. These experiences evolved into a social pattern helped by many geographical moves, making myself so agreeable with each new set of people that I always got on well for the first few weeks. Then people would become aware of my strangeness because it was impossible to hide it completely. Someone would notice, and it took only one. Then I would sense I was being watched which, in turn, increased my tension, and so on, ad infinitum.

When I was about eighteen, I met a young man at work who I became particularly drawn to. He seemed to understand and sympathise with my shyness and inability to relax in the company of others, and he seemed untroubled by my facial twitches, which I confess I reduced to a minimum whenever he was around. He would use the flimsiest of excuses to approach me and took pains to get me to talk. I began to feel that here was someone who would accept me for what I was, and in the manner of the young and naive, I began to believe in the saving graces of true love. When he asked for a date, I reached an incredible high. This was beyond my wildest dreams and I was convinced that my knight in shining armour was about to sweep away all my fears and support and share my burden. I even thought that with his help I would see my torment vanquished forever. Either he was a direct gift from God, sent to put an end to my painful existence, or we would become so close, he would simply make a nonsense of it. My life suddenly seemed to have some happiness in store. I was ecstatic, and in my eagerness to experience normal teenage behaviour which I could see going on all around me, I relaxed when the big occasion arrived.

Cars being few and far between in those days, I tried to manoeuvre our seating on the bus so that my companion would be placed on my left side, away from my right arm which has always been more uncontrollable than my left, but the bus was busy and I was unsuccessful. However, for what seemed like the first time in my life I was free of the crippling anxiety which normally dogged my every moment, and I did not care, especially when he took hold of my right hand and held it in a firm grip. "Dare I believe this?" I thought. With the natural optimism of youth I did believe it, and when he released my hand to pay for the tickets, and my arm, already champing at the bit, took advantage of the sudden freedom to behave in its usual way by attacking my right breast, I was not unduly alarmed, simply trapping it in my lap with my left hand. I then lifted my eyes to look out of the window while I waited. It was dark outside and I was able to see a perfect reflection of my companion and the ticket collector. Within a single heartbeat I knew my worst fears had returned. It was a moment of stricken tableau. The conductor was motionless and my companion looked as if he had been turned to stone. Our eyes met in the mirrored glass for one horrific instant. Then, with a drop in my spirits that was like a physical blow, the beautiful dream was scattered like late blossom in a sudden gust of wind.

The rest of the journey was completed in silence and a fury of facial tics, my right arm tucked firmly under my left elbow. The young man withdrew to a point light years away and on arriving at our destination I pleaded a sick headache and was ushered, with excruciating politeness, into a taxi. The following morning I phoned my employer with the excuse of a family crisis preventing my return, and had the distinct impression that my decision was not only expected, but also welcomed.

Other jobs followed, all in the same pattern. In an endeavour to improve my lot, I attended night school to learn how to type. The worst skill I could possibly attempt to learn, but in my usual fashion of ignoring my condition because any day could bring about a miracle, I stayed long enough to learn the basics. I knew I could never be a typist, let alone a secretary, but I decided to register with an agency for temporary work, filling in for holidays, etc. Convinced that I had found the perfect solution, in that each position would last only a week or two, and perseverance being the name of the game, I turned up for my first job in a good frame of mind. It was with dismay that I realised the assistant whose absence I was filling had her desk in the same office as her boss, at right angles to his! There was no way I could hide my affliction. I had refused any job that entailed working in an open plan office, but had taken it for granted that in this instance, I would be in an office by myself. I did the best I could and after a few shocked glances in my direction, the poor man got on with his work.

By the end of the day I had achieved very little, because each time I returned the carriage of the typewriter, my hand had to have a dozen or so bangs at my chest before I could begin a new line, resulting in a panic to get started again. This, in turn, resulted in many mistakes and retyping of pages. But I dared to think I might get through the week. When I arrived the next morning I found my desk and typewriter gone. On my employer's desk there was a note to the effect that they had been moved to an empty office and would I please work there. I appreciated his kindness in allowing me to carry on at all, but the whole thing was a nightmare and I rang the agency immediately for a replacement.

No job I tackled lasted long and I began to realise that working for my living was not really going to be possible, but there was no alternative, except for the unthinkable. As for my secret desire to be a teacher, something I always felt I would be good at, the idea of me standing in front of a classroom full of children was laughable. Unfortunately, staying at home was not an alternative either, since the lack of communication between my parents and me was total. Then I saw an advert for women to join the Armed Forces, and with the impulsiveness and flood of hope so symptomatic of TS, I joined.

The period of initial training was not too bad. Although I was in a large dormitory, the pattern associated with a new environment again established itself, and the speed of our activities, so typical of training in the Forces, was such that no one had time to spare a glance for anyone else. Even marching, which I would have thought impossible for me, was not so. Standing rigidly to attention is the easiest stance for me, and the fast motion of the march, the easiest way to move.

But the day came when I had to move on to my first posting and from the moment I arrived I knew that, despite any initial relief, I was in for it, and so it proved. Then God intervened again. Having absolutely no control over my life because of a signed contract, making it impossible for me to run away again, I discovered that I could escape into almost permanent night duty. It was my custom to do whole stretches of them alone, since in the event of anyone being with me, it was not difficult to persuade them to 'get their head down'. Refusals were rare, and night duty became a life-saver. Another was badminton. I drifted into the gymnasium one day and stood watching a game of badminton. Seeing my interest, the sports officer suggested I try it, and for want of a reasonable excuse, I picked up a racquet and discovered something fabulous. On the court I could hammer out all my frustrations and I became a fierce opponent.

The sad part is that I did not realise what I was doing at the time, I was aware only that my future no longer felt so bleak and empty. Tourettes did not go away and I was caught out many times with the feeling of shame and embarrassment no less than it had always been, but the solitude of night duty and the release of tension provided by my badminton racquet, soon restored my equilibrium. However, it was during those lonely nights that I started the practice of compulsive eating.

Coping with TS is like a long and difficult labour – the concentration needed to get through the pain and struggle is all embracing. How can I explain how I managed to function as a wife and mother, albeit very badly, without creating a sense of disbelief? Yet I did, but each family crisis that arose increased the intensity of my condition, causing a complete breakdown of my marriage within a few years. This, in turn, brought about the worst period of my condition in my entire adult life and the concentration needed in order to keep control of my crazy behaviour created a spiral of selfish introspection, which ruined my children's early years. It must have been very miserable indeed, to grow up in a household so completely lacking in laughter or light-heartedness of any kind.

There were only three occasions when I attempted to seek medical help during all the years before TS was finally diagnosed. When I was in my twenties, with two young babies, my mother-in-law persuaded me to see a psychiatrist. Then I saw another a few years later after the birth of my third child, and finally during the first year or so after my husband and I had parted for good.

On the first occasion, I realise now that I was in a serious clinical depression, though at the time I had never heard of such a thing. I could not speak and had not done so for some time, either to my children or my in-laws with whom I was living while my husband was abroad. I was like a robot. On my arrival at the clinic I could not give my name to the receptionist and my identity was established through her kindness and the use of her pen as a pointer. I was in the psychiatrist's office for less than ten minutes, still unable to speak, and was then told that if I refused to speak I could not be helped, and was shown out. I remember walking along the hospital corridor, stunned, considering the effort it had cost me to get there, and appealing with my eyes to every white-coated person I passed, for help.

On the second occasion, the psychiatrist listened kindly to everything I said and listed my habits as I related them, and a further appointment was made. When I returned, I was seen by a student and asked if I had any objection to her recording the interview, which I did not. She then asked me to repeat the list of my habits. When I had finished, her repeated questions, "Is that all? Are there any more?" at first surprised me. Then her insistence frightened me, to the point where I believed I was doing something very wrong. Days later, I remembered that I had forgotten to mention two of my habits which I had given during my previous visit, and I do not remember seeing that psychiatrist again.

My final attempt came to another abrupt end when I was asked to pick up a pencil from the desk in front of me and hand it to the psychiatrist. When I did so without apparent difficulty, I received a lecture on wasting his time and was again shown the door. Unfortunately, he had no way of knowing that my short periods of control had become second nature to me, and I was unable to tell him. None of these interviews made me angry, however, because I understood the lack of understanding. After all, I could not understand myself, so could hardly expect anyone else to do so. I blamed myself for my inability to explain my condition, or convince the professionals and struggled on as I always had until the day I first heard the words 'Tourette Syndrome'.

Most of today's children who suffer from TS do not have to spend their days fearing they are mad, although diagnosis is far from automatic. The thought of any child going through my experiences strikes a coldness in me that would freeze hell. When I was young, a film was made about the conditions under which patients suffered in the mental asylums of the day, as they were then called. It was frighteningly frank and shocking and caused a great furore upon its release. For my part, the film strongly reinforced my belief that I had better conceal my own 'madness', or that was likely where I would end up. It terrified me.

However the Tourette Syndrome (UK) Association now exists, (with its counterparts in other countries, chiefly the USA) which, with the help of its magazine *Antics*, gives help and encouragement to sufferers and, very importantly, their families. This concern for the family stems from the fact that TS creates havoc and tremendous mental strain for everyone, not just those unfortunate enough to be born with it. The sufferers suffer on two fronts, however, for they are fully aware of the effect their condition has on those around them, so suffer also for those they love and depend on.

Antics includes reports from doctors and researchers, passing on their ever-increasing knowledge of TS, as well as the latest means of combating its effects. Questionnaires from professionals such as these are sent out so that there is a constant gathering of information, and some offer their services free in special clinics. There is also a *Directory of Contacts*, listing the names and addresses of sufferers, and providing a wonderful opportunity to share the burden. The following passages nearly blew my mind when I read them in *Antics,* so completely did they echo the story of my life:

Gilles de la Tourette Syndrome is a movement disorder characterised by repeated, involuntary, rapid movements of various muscle groups and by vocal tics such as barking, sniffing or grunting. The syndrome is a lifelong disorder that often begins during adolescence with eye spasms. Tourettes individuals ... may have an increased incidence of compulsive rituals and Agoraphobia, although the role of these disorders in the disease is not understood.

Up to 50% of all children with TS also have ADHD (Attention Deficit Hyperactivity Disorder), which is manifested by problems with attention span, concentration, distractibility, impulsivity and motor hyperactivity. Attentional problems often precede the onset of TS symptoms and may worsen as the tics develop. The increasing difficulty with attention may reflect an underlying biological dysfunction involving inhibition and may be exacerbated by the strain of attending to the outside world while working hard to remain still and quiet. Attentional problems and hyperactivity can profoundly affect school achievement. At least 30-40% of TS children have serious school performance handicaps that require special interventions, and children with both TS and ADHD are especially vulnerable to long term educational impairment. Attention deficits may persist into adulthood and together with compulsions and obsessions, can seriously impair job performance.

So there it all is in a nutshell. All these things are part of my make-up, and the attention deficit factor no doubt accounts for my lifelong appalling memory, in the sense that I have not so much forgotten things, but have not taken them in properly in the first place. For example, on a broader level, the Sixties era, talked of so much today in terms of flower power, hippie communes and permissiveness, for me just did not happen. I was totally unaware of it, and I have no idea where I was, or what I was doing on the day President Kennedy died. There was simply no room for anything other than the total concentration needed to stay on top of my very limited world, the foundations of which were so desperately shaky.

Tourette Syndrome has been the single most important thing in my life, as inevitable as breathing and sleeping, but there has also been a strangeness in my life which is very difficult to explain. It is as if I have lived in a parallel world in which I have absorbed the actions and words of those travelling alongside me, and then acted out the expected behaviour. But that was not the real me, and somehow people sense that the image I am presenting is a false image and, therefore, to be distrusted. I believe them to think me insincere, and in an odd way that is true. But insincerity is the wrong word and I cannot think of the right word to express it. Except, perhaps, doppelganger, that wraith of a living person which gives the impression of things not being what they seem, or the changes a chameleon makes to blend in with its surroundings in order to protect itself. One of the things which has made it possible for me to get as far as I have, has been my ability to give the lie to my condition, to consciously deny that it was happening, and banish it from my mind. Maybe that was why I found it so difficult to talk to psychiatrists because I had, from childhood, trained myself to think of myself as normal. But then, what choice did I have?

Today I can talk freely about TS for quite lengthy periods, but not if I am questioned as if in interrogation. Perhaps for the same reason, specific and repeated questioning causes a panic attack, which makes my brain shut down. My mind goes completely blank and I am left feeling foolish and inadequate again. TS has marred all the relationships that are important to all people. Alienated from my parents and older siblings early in life, it has continued to punish those I love most of all, and me too. I suspect that other TS sufferers of my generation have also experienced the lack of love and affection that has been my lot, and the sadness of being unable to express affection for those closest to us. It is only in the last two or three years that I have known what it is like to hug and be hugged, and I realise how much I have missed. But I blame no one but myself for this, because TS forced me to stay aloof. Letting down my guard, my rigidity, would have meant the demons taking over completely and that was always out of the question.

However, my consultant was right when he told me that the condition eases with age. I have been settled in one place for some years now and have put down practical and financial roots that make it impossible for me to run away again. During this time there has been a slow release from what I think of as a 'paralysis of life', but it is clear that I am fated never to be completely in charge. TS has always dictated how my life will run its course and, seemingly, always will; and to quote the words of Chris Mansley, a fellow sufferer, 'the psychological and emotional scars will never heal'. I am still possessed, though to a lesser degree, by behavioural problems which cause people to be uncomfortable and sometimes distance themselves, and I lack the social graces which come with a properly balanced maturity.

As for my children, their kindness towards me, in view of my complete lack of motherly qualities when they were young, amazes me, though it is obvious that TS frightens them so that communication between us is always on a very shallow level. But I brought them up alone and my domestic circumstances were so stressful that, at the time, the barrier between me and the outside world was at its widest. I must have appeared uninterested in their lives, but I did my best within the confines of an illness I did not know I had, and the fugue-like state of my days caused by years of hangovers from heavy night-time sedation. No one will ever know how difficult that was and there was no one there to help. For someone like me to have to cope alone with three children was enough, but to also have to work full time was extreme, and I do not know how I survived.

It was during these years that I went through the gamut of sleeping pills. Barbiturates were often given together, so that at one time I was found to be suffering from barbiturate poisoning. For years I took Mandrax and Mogadon – subsequently put on the dangerous drugs list. Sleeping at night has never been easy. Every night, still, and for as far back as I can remember, just as I am drifting off, a nerve explodes at the base of my skull, causing a convulsion which is like being struck by a sledgehammer, and I am wide awake again. If I were standing on my feet it would knock me over. This can happen a few, or many times, depending on my level of stress and tiredness that day, as does its intensity. It is quite common for it to cause my whole body to leave the surface of my bed, and sleep does not come until the sleeping draught crashes in and zonks me out. Nevertheless, sleep was what stopped me from tipping over the edge of sanity.

At evenings and weekends, during the long years I brought my children up alone, I would often lie on my stomach on the living room floor and sleep deeply for hours. They would come and go around me doing whatever was necessary for themselves, even watching television over my prone form. Such a thing would not be allowed to happen today, any more than the reaction I received from my doctor when I turned to alcohol and went to him because I was getting through two bottles of vodka a week. I reasoned that though help with my weirdness was not forthcoming, perhaps I might get it as an offshoot from alcoholism. What I did not expect was to be laughed at and told to come back when I was drinking two bottles a day. But it all had to end, and eventually I switched off and found myself turning away from my children altogether.

Unforgivably, I began to neglect them thoroughly, and as the months went by and I could see what I was doing to them, and knew that what I was doing was alien to my nature, again I reached the point of suicide. But I could not bring myself to do it any more than I ever had, so I persuaded myself that the best thing I could do for them was to remove myself completely from their lives. I walked out on them in what, at the time, I believed to be the best way possible, but which I realise now was unbelievably cruel. Their suffering must have been acute and I do not deserve the loving attention I get from them today. Looking back, I can see how unnatural my behaviour was. I treated it as though the whole thing was a game, as if everyone was going on holiday, as if I was enjoying the prospect of it all and so should they. I could see their apprehension, their anxiety and their distress, but it meant nothing to me. I felt nothing. Perhaps I had gone into another robot-like state. I do not know.

The strange thing is that I cannot remember anything about the day we parted. I do not know where I left my children, or how I left them, and cannot even remember saying goodbye. The day it happened is a complete blank. It was the worst act of my entire life and I am forever haunted by remorse and regret. But now that I am capable of speaking out in my own defence, I have to say that I find it hard to take all the blame.

Throughout my entire life, one of my biggest compulsions, or screaming needs, as I tend to think of them, has been to stand or sit, always, at the back of any room or hall in the right hand corner. This is not only so that I can judge the exact split second when the gaze of everyone present is directed away from me so that I can sneak in a quick tic, but because if there is anyone behind me, I am overcome with feelings of stress and panic so strong I am forced to move, if necessary out of the room. I have even been forced to ask for a desk in that position when sitting an exam because had I not done so, my performance would have been even more flawed than usual, as most of my concentration would have been spent on controlling my arm movements and checking over my shoulder whether or not I was being watched, leaving little attention for the work in front of me.

It has not helped that I have never learned to be sound in judgement or logical in my reasoning, which has made decision-making extremely hazardous. In fact, my mind is like a grasshopper who has had one too many. I have blundered from one crisis to another, and in attempting to cover up my mistakes, I have developed a brashness of manner, which is not easy to like. Laughter is very difficult for me because it feels unnatural, and I have to make a conscious effort to smile. This always feels more like a grimace and the lack of spontaneity means that there are times when I should smile but do not, which creates difficulties for others because they are unable to tell in what sense I mean the words that I am saying.

Staying out of the mainstream of life has been automatic; so that I have not been able to do many of the things other people take for granted. Like going to the theatre, which, given the chance, I would do as often as possible. But, the moment the curtain goes up, I am flooded with the urge to jerk my head. Up, down, from side to side, escalating to my whole body wanting to jerk itself away from contact with my seat. On the odd occasion I have tried it, I have barely been conscious of what was happening on stage. My whole concentration has been on the horror of waiting for the humiliation of someone behind me uttering loudly those words, which have echoed through all my ages, "Will you keep still?" However, such is the perversity of my condition that, on first settling in this area, I paid a fee to become a 'friend' of the local theatre, which entitled me to various advantages, including cheap tickets. I suppressed the knowledge that it was a nonsensical thing to do, believing quite earnestly that I would make full use of the concessions. But I did not use my membership once. This illustrates what I see as the dichotomy of the TS mind. The hope that keeps it going, moving hand in hand with the acceptance of reality, the desire to opt out of life, whilst grasping the desperate need to prove that one's life has not been totally futile, and the urge to express the personal fulfilment you know you are capable of, but which you are prevented from doing by something inexplicable.

Now I find myself wanting to do all the active and adventurous things I yearned to do when I was younger, but that dichotomy is still in force, in a way, because my body no longer has the strength to attempt them. Nevertheless, I am experiencing many firsts, and have achieved a stronger hold over my physical aberrations, enough to enable me to join in the activities of a busy, caring community, although occasionally I feel the need to isolate myself, and do so to allow myself a little respite. Then I pick up where I left off and it does not seem to matter. What does matter, what is so very important, is that, although I understand why, it is difficult to deal with the reluctance of my family and others, to talk about my condition. The refusal to acknowledge TS does an injustice to many thousands of people, because it does exist and is not going to be beaten without a lot of help, and I feel that I have struggled too hard and too long to allow my life with TS to go unheeded. Everyone needs to be valued, and in my opinion, every life has a meaning.

I find it difficult to understand why the condition is not more widely acknowledged. For, except for those involved in my initial diagnosis, every doctor has referred to my condition as depression. I have smarted a little about this and on once mentioning it, was told that the term Tourette Syndrome was unacceptable because no one knew what it meant. Then, recently, I picked up a leaflet on future care, published by a private medical insurance company, in response to the increased difficulties the NHS is experiencing in caring for the elderly. This excludes any 'mental or nervous disorder, which cannot be shown to be due to an organic brain disease or brain injury', and one of the examples of this exclusion is depression. So where, I ask, does that leave people like me? It has been firmly established for a long time now that people are born with TS, yet if I was financially able to avail myself of this service, I might not be able to do so. We do seem to have the odds stacked against us.

However, despite my prison-like existence, my thanks go out to God for allowing me to live long enough to clarify a lifetime of bewilderment, and for giving me the strength to control my condition in those far-off days when help from any source was nonexistent. Controlling my habits myself has been truly essential, since the alternative was too awful to contemplate, but the cost in terms of the rest of my life has been very high, and when He decides that my day has come, I will leave here with the sense of going home after a long and trying excursion. 'Whosoever believeth in Me shall not perish'. These words have always meant a lot to me. But if someone begged the questions, "Can't you just stop, like people stop smoking?", or, "Since you haven't been able to lead a normal life, haven't you perished anyway?" My answer to the first question would be, "Only if I stop breathing". To the second question my answer would be, "No, I have not". For I believe that we are all put on this earth for a purpose, as part of the progression of mankind, which it is not our privilege to know. We do have a freedom of choice, but the future must always remain a mystery for the present. If that were not so, life would be pointless and the qualities of ambition and achievement pointless also. The TS sufferer does not have that freedom of choice to anything like the same extent as normal people, but, despite this, I see my role in life as a definite participant in that progression. I shall never know, on earth, that is, how my own purpose has been defined, but I see my experiences with TS as being as important in the progress of mankind as any discovery in any field. It has been God's will, and I will know why all in good time.

When I first had the idea to write about Tourette Syndrome, it was obvious that I could not do it in the form of an academic treatise or report. Instead, I have simply told my story as best I can and hope that it will not be viewed as a vehicle for self-pity. That has certainly not been my intention, for I have always thanked God that I was not born blind or deaf, and have done my best to cope with my limitations with as little complaint as possible. My intention, in fact, in laying bare my soul in respect of TS, has been to help bring about a wider and deeper understanding of the syndrome with its strictures of silence and isolation. My fervent hope is that, by doing so, I will also help to bring about the discovery of whatever is responsible for such cruel destruction of potentiality, by appealing for financial assistance in order to keep research and the Tourettes Association in operation, for they are in serious danger of having to close down for lack of funds.

The complexity of TS leaves everyone who comes into contact with it bewildered, or devastated, depending on their level of involvement. It is not a fatal condition, in that people do not die from it, and there are some who manage to overcome it and make a success of their lives in creative and professional ways, becoming artists or even surgeons, as Dr Oliver Sacks relates in his book *An Anthropologist on Mars*. But many people who are born with severe TS are completely crushed by its relentless and unceasing power, and can lead lives of appalling loneliness.

So if, by telling my tale, I have also encouraged other sufferers to realise that they are not alone in their strangeness, and to recognise that, worldwide, there are probably millions like us, then that is a bonus. This is my prayer, and may God see His way to grant it one day.

NOT A SAD STORY

Sam's Story by his Mum

"Sam," I hissed angrily, "you don't push other children over. I've told you a million times, why don't you listen?" With that, I gave him a big push to show him just how it felt, and he sat down with a plonk. Sam was three years old, a lovely little boy to look at, always busy and happy. He rarely cried about anything, but as soon as he got into a group of children, he went haywire and started to cause trouble. His way of telling another child that he wanted to play was to give them a big push. The child would fall over, then rush for his mother and the end result was not the desired one. No one wanted to play with this outgoing happy little chap!

This was the start of some lonely and difficult years for Sam. The pushing started as soon as he could walk, and made toddler group – which I quickly abandoned – then play group – a nightmare. Four weeks after entry into infant school, Sam's teacher told us that Sam was aggressive, and his social skills were very poor. We had hoped that growing into a four-and-a-half-year-old and going to 'big' school would be the answer for Sam and settle him. Instead, for the two and a half years he was in that first school, his behaviour remained difficult and my self-esteem as a mum fell lower and lower. After all, it must be my fault; other mums looked at me and their faces told me that. The headmistress and teachers must have gauged the same. I was so demoralised.

Our hopes had started high having Sam. I had been so desperate to have a family. I loved the company of children and knew from my own experience that family life could be very good and incomplete without children. When Dave and I had been married for eight years, it was confirmed to us that we could never have children and it was a long wait, another five years, before we were thrilled one day in January 1988 to have a phone call from the adoption agency. There was a baby due in a month and his mum was sure that adoption was right for him. Were we interested? The social worker gave us some details about his parents. Yes, we were interested, and that month was a very long one until Sam was eventually born, two weeks late, on a snowy February day.

Our memories of collecting this tiny baby are of a very cold, crisp, sunny day with crocuses everywhere, and dressing Sam up ourselves out of his hospital clothes in the special care baby unit, into tiny babygros which I had been collecting for months. He was three days old and we loved him straight away. By six weeks old, he was so alert and active. When he cried for milk he meant five minutes ago. And at six weeks old he started to play knocking down towers of bricks. We were thrilled. I had told Dave it would be good, and it was, until Sam started to walk at fifteen months and wreak havoc whenever any other children were about.

Sam stayed at his first school for two and a half years. I spent much of that time helping in class, and watching over him at lunch-time in the playground along with Jenny, his little sister, who came along exactly three years after him. Sam's headmistress told me, "Sam is difficult, you can always pick him out in a classroom as soon as you walk in. He will always look different." The difference wasn't physical; he looked very 'normal'. It was his behaviour. He roamed the classroom and rarely sat. On the mat, with thirty other children, he was a disaster, as he could not keep still. He would kick with his feet, or irritate other children. He would often be in trouble for inappropriate behaviour in the playground. He just never seemed to get the idea of how to relate to other children. I watched Jenny do it and she was three years younger. Why couldn't Sam tow the line?

There were times in those two and a half years when I screamed and screamed at Sam in frustration. I spent lots of time with both children playing with them, and I carefully talked behaviour through with Sam. He seemed to understand and take it on board, and then there he was in trouble again! The downward spiral at this first school escalated one cold February morning when I was again helping in school. I had been called in to see the headmistress after school the previous day. Sam had been angry in the playground and had unpopped another little boy's hood from his anorak and thrown it into the snow. He had already been sent to the head himself, they had asked me to punish him too.

The following morning, after the teacher had finished talking to the rest of the class on the mat around her, she said, "Sam, I believe we have some unfinished business, come and stand here." She called the other little boy involved to the front. She meant to help, but the outcome was that Sam was publicly humiliated in front of thirty children. No one by this time would even consider that he might have a reasonable explanation. He took the blame for anything by now, even if he was nowhere near the scene of the crime. Children would say, "Sam did it" and no adult questioned the statement any more. So far, a small incident, no one had been hurt, and one that any other 'normal' child might also have committed. Sam was punished three times over the course of two days. He was seven years old, all but a few days, and life at that school finished that day.

Amazingly, when Sam took some 'goodbye' sweets in to say that he was leaving, half the children came out of that class in a state of disbelief saying, "Sam can't leave," "Don't let him leave," "We like Sam." He was fun and I think he filled the role of class entertainer for them too. When things got too boring, he performed some antic to lighten the atmosphere, and loved to play to an audience and make people laugh. I was very touched by their affection, when the only message I had received from school was a negative one. So we started a new era at another local primary school.

We had high hopes, a new chance, a new start where no one knew Sam, in a school where staff were sympathetic to what we had been through, and seemed to have more expertise in handling children who didn't quite fit the mould. We explained to Sam, that this was a new start, not to repeat past mistakes, that he could be very happy there. And at the start, he was. Leaving the first school, there was hardly any work to take with him. Here he was producing quite a lot. Yes, this teacher had it under her control, and things were better for a while. We were only called in to ask if we could have a word with Sam about throwing the little counters they had for maths. We were hopeful and told everyone. It was just the school that was wrong, Sam is fine in this new environment, but it didn't last.

In the next school year, and with a change of teacher (something that always unsettled Sam a lot, as any change in routine did), we were again called in about antisocial behaviour, namely, nipping other children. I had found by this time, as with the pushing behaviour, that the only way to help Sam understand that this was a 'no', was to do it to him. So I pushed him, bit him and nipped him, as he did to others. I hated doing it. It was against all I felt about 'proper' mothering, but was the only thing that worked.

That autumn something else happened. It was half term and we were staying with my sister for a few days and visiting old friends. Sam seemed very on edge. He was very difficult to handle and explosive over small things. Why? I am very placid and patient by temperament. Why couldn't I meet this little boy's needs? We were out in a playground and there he was, shaking his head, again and again. Was there something really wrong with him? I began to worry and worry. You see, the head shaking was chronic and very noticeable to anyone else in the playground. That night, I sat up all night with him, watching him, but it didn't happen whilst he was asleep. Then on waking, it started up again. Had he got a brain tumour? Had he got some terrible neurological disorder? We were frantic, and that day, I took Sam to our local casualty. They checked him thoroughly. Nothing seemed wrong to them, and certainly not life threatening. I was reassured, but still went to our local GP and reported it with some of our other troubles.

There was just something with Sam that you couldn't pinpoint. Why did he drink so much? Why didn't he go to sleep at night? Why did he hate bright lights, and why was he so terrified of sudden loud noises? Why was his social behaviour so poor? Our local GP wrote to the children's hospital and, in summary, we had our first trip to see the psychologist and a neurological paediatrician. By this time, the head shaking was long past. It had lasted for about three weeks and stopped as fast as it had started. I was tempted to think that it was nothing after all, but decided we might as well go ahead with the appointment anyway. Sam had six sessions with the psychologist, and play therapy to try to improve his social understanding. She admitted defeat!

In the following April, when he was eight years old, he received a full, two-day assessment at the children's hospital. Jiggling around my childcare, I dropped off Sam and Jenny with Dave, and ran back to the hospital for the conclusions from the two-day assessment. All the specialists had had a good look at him – physiotherapists, occupational therapists, ear people, eye people, and the doctor specialising in neurological disorders. I arrived late, puffing, sat down next to half a dozen specialists, waiting to hear what they had to say. Yes, his communication skills were poor for someone of his age, but they could find nothing wrong with him. He was just at the far end of the normal spectrum.

We carried on with no further help for another nine months. We had better moments. He went into a new class, Year 4, with a wonderful teacher who believed that praise and encouragement were the best ways to make children perform well. Her strategy was right; Sam would have swung from the ceiling for her. He loved to get 'smiley faces' and we glowed at the Christmas concert when he was entrusted with a small part. He glowed too.

In January 1997, we had a review meeting with Sam's teacher, and the special educational needs co-ordinator at the school. They were so pleased with his progress that he would go down on the special needs register from stage two to stage one, and she was confident that very soon he wouldn't need to be on the register at all. We were over the moon. We really thought that our troubles were all in the past and that it was simply late maturing that had caused all our problems.

We were wrong! For some reason, in January 1997, at nearly nine, Sam's problems suddenly escalated. In class, he found it very difficult to sit for more than a couple of minutes and was constantly roaming, demanding the teacher's attention, unable to complete any work, and making lots of repetitive little noises, blowing raspberries and squeaking. He was disciplined, but the behaviour just got worse, and again began a negative spiral and we had to admit defeat. We had to withdraw Sam from school.

In the meantime, a friend had lent me a book about Attention Deficit Disorder. Her son is also adopted and was similarly struggling at school and he had been diagnosed and was being treated for ADD. I read the book. Sam jumped out of every page at me! I rang back to the hospital where Sam had had his assessment. Did he have ADD? I asked. Yes, they said. They had picked this up at his assessment, although they were unwilling to put a label of ADD on children at that time. I was relieved, at last we now knew that Sam's problem was real and not his fault, but simply part of his make-up and we could start to get some real help for him.

However, as I continued to read the book, the words 'Tourette Syndrome' kept popping up. What was this? It wasn't clear. I investigated further and suddenly, everything made sense. This was Sam. A typical Tourettes sufferer with ADD as a part of the syndrome. The vocal noises he got into trouble for at school, and the head shaking were not put on, but involuntary tics. We returned to the neurological paediatrician we had seen a year earlier and he confirmed it positively. Although it was devastating, it was also a relief. Sam had an inherited condition that made his life at school a very difficult one. He couldn't do his work and he couldn't succeed with friends in the playground at this time. He needed help.

It was at this time that I had a chance meeting with a friend I hadn't seen for a long time in a queue in McDonald's. I was so miserable and when she asked how I was, I admitted how low I felt. "Come and see me at school," said Janice. So a few days later I did. Janice teaches at a secondary school for about a hundred special needs children and the caring atmosphere immediately struck me. They understood the needs of their pupils, some of whom were quite difficult. They did not offload the children's difficulties on to the parents, which had so often been my experience. In this school they saw the children as individuals, and also tried to provide them with a social life, planning treats and outings for them. I was very impressed. "Why don't you look at special schooling for Sam?" suggested Janice, and she gave me a list of special schools in our town. But what type of school is suitable for a child with an unusual disorder like Tourette Syndrome?

About two miles from our home, I noticed there was a small, special, integrated resource unit for children with Dyslexia within a normal mainstream school. I visited a few days later and loved it. Each of the ten children in the unit had been through a difficult experience at school and had become demoralised and often rejected by other children. The two skilled staff in the unit were not only addressing their Dyslexia, but also their damaged self-esteem. There was an air of peace in this attractively laid-out classroom, with pictures all around the walls, and the children looked happy. I was very impressed.

For the next six months, the process of getting an Educational Statement of Special Need for Sam trundled slowly on. Fortunately the paediatrician had said this was essential which helped the process a lot. I taught him at home. He spent very little time at school in these last months and was very anxious about it when he did, although once the staff understood that he had a real disorder, and was not simply being naughty, they tried extremely hard to meet his needs.

In September 1997, his statement was approved and he started in the integrated resource unit at the new school. As I write, it is now nine months since Sam started at his third primary school. At last, he has found real happiness in the classroom, and his teachers too are amazed at how he has settled down. From the distraught little boy who arrived in September, to a child who can now cope so much better with all aspects of school life, even to taking some lessons in a mainstream classroom again. A year ago, we would not have believed this could ever be possible. Sam's teachers have a reward system with stickers, and Sam is now on his second sheet. He is so proud, and we are too.

1997 was a very difficult year for us all as a family, coming to terms with Sam's disorder. At ten years old, he is very self-aware too. It has not been easy for him. His motor tics were very severe in 1997, as well as his difficult behaviour. His whole body seemed to be alive with them, and anyone who saw him immediately recognised that there was something wrong with him. His arms would suddenly shoot out, or he bounced on his bottom, unable to sit still, and also made a wide range of squeaks and purrs and other vocalisations.

Gradually, since September 1997, the body tics, and as I presently write (June 1998) even the vocal tics, have almost disappeared, as Sam's stress levels have fallen. The integrated resource is a safe, secure and caring haven for children like Sam, where he is accepted for being uniquely Sam. Now he can sit and complete his work, and he takes great pride in it. He has made friends and developed an enthusiastic interest in football. We are so proud of him, and so are his teachers. We want to support him through school – at the present moment this means finding a secondary school where he can be comfortable, accepted and helped.

This is not supposed to be a sad story, although, as any parent feels when their child is discovered to have something wrong with him, we wish he did not have to cope with Tourette Syndrome. Sometimes I watch the children of friends and wish Sam didn't have to struggle so much to achieve what comes so easily to them. But we wouldn't want to change Sam either. He has always been a lovely little person, full of ideas for games and with a big sense of fun. He loves life and is never bored. We want to give him a very happy childhood with lots of memories of fun, in a safe and secure environment and with our unconditional love, and help him to socialise successfully. My worst nightmare is that he should be lonely.

What will the future hold for him? Ever since he was very small, he has had a fascination with the emergency services, especially the fire service. He is very calm and capable in a crisis, eager to take command and very sensible. Maybe this is where he will find his place in adult life. Maybe this is where some of his *disability* will actually perform in adult life as *ability*?

We look forward to finding out.

THE CLOUDS ARE LIFTING

Sophie's Story by her Mum

I often used to say to my husband, with a slight sense of unease, that we were leading a charmed life. We were so happy with our lives together, a happiness intensified by the arrival of our two beautiful, healthy children, first our son, Jack, and then, two and a half years later, our daughter, Sophie.

We made all the usual mistakes that young parents make, but delighted in watching the children grow up. Like all doting parents, and probably much to the disgust of our childless friends, our conversation revolved around the children. If one of us had been out, we would be greeted on our return with an up-to-the-minute account of what our little darlings had been up to while we were away.

And so it continued. Life was good. As they developed, it was obvious that they were both going to be little live wires. Jack, in particular, was sociable to the extent that wherever we went, he would announce, from a very early age, that he was, "going to find a friend". Within minutes, he would be happily chatting to a suitable candidate and organising a game of some kind. They were both very bright and artistic and, in Sophie's case, musical. Most important of all, they were both healthy and happy.

Again, just occasionally, a slight shadow of unease would flit across this untroubled scene – what had we done to deserve all this? Could such happiness and contentment really last?

Both children sailed through junior school with just the usual ups and downs until, in Sophie's last year, her popularity suddenly took a nose-dive and she became somewhat isolated from her peers. She found this very distressing, as she had always been in the thick of things.

Jack, meanwhile, had transferred to secondary school without a ripple. He had achieved a place at a selective boys' grammar school of his own choosing, where the strict discipline put a bit of a break on his natural exuberance, but it proved to be a place where he could develop and learn and make many good friends.

The choice of secondary school for Sophie presented more of a problem. The local comprehensive did not have a very good academic record, so, as non-churchgoers, our only alternative was a fee-paying, all-girls high school. If she had been getting on better with her schoolmates, we might have been persuaded to send her to the comp, but we felt strongly that she should be given equal opportunities with her brother. So she took and passed the entrance exam, and the high school it was.

Since she was about four, Sophie had had a tiny wart, right on the end of her nose. She had had it frozen off more times than we cared to count, and it had always returned after a short interval. She was desperate that her 'bobble' as we called it, should be permanently removed before she started at the new school. An attempt to slice it off in out-patients resulted in near hysteria, despite Sophie having an oversized teddy bear thrust into her arms by the nurse. Barely disguising her impatience, the doctor said she would have to have it removed under general anaesthetic. The operation was carried out, much to Sophie's relief, during the summer holidays.

As an additional preparation for secondary school, both Sophie and Jack received the MMR (Measles, Mumps and Rubella) jab, having discussed the pros and cons with our GP. I have since wondered if either the anaesthetic, or the jab might have triggered Sophie's illness, since we only noticed the head-shaking after she started secondary school. However, Sophie remembers repeatedly scrunching up her nose and trying to look down it while she was at junior school. Apparently her friends used to remark on it.

We have a photograph of Sophie on the morning of her first day at her new school. She looks desperately unhappy and I agonised over whether we had done the right thing. I remember taking her to the school like a lamb to the slaughter. She would be the second youngest child in her year, as her birthday is in late August, and in many ways seemed too young to be starting secondary school. Would she make friends? Would she be happy? Would she do well?

Almost immediately after she had started at the school, Sophie started shaking her head in a strange, repetitive way. She was growing out her fringe at the time and it was falling into her eyes, and I put it down to that. It soon became so pronounced that I eventually suggested that she have a perm (something I would never normally have allowed at that age) to stop her hair from flopping into her eyes. Still the head-shaking continued, becoming more frequent and pronounced. I tried all the usual things to try and make her stop, such as, at first, ignoring it, then bribing her with little rewards and even, to my shame, shouting at her, as it irritated everyone in the household. It never occurred to me that it might be something over which she had no control.

However, Sophie seemed to be settling well into her new school and had made lots of new friends, but after just three months, the headmistress called us in. Apparently she had lost virtually every book and piece of gym kit, and she wanted to make us aware of the problem so that it could be nipped in the bud. We were not alarmed, if anything we were slightly amused, it was so typical of Sophie's dreamy approach to life.

What we did not know, but Sophie has since told us, was that the head-shaking had now become so bad in school that other children had started to notice. They would ask what she was doing, not in a nasty way, more out of curiosity. But Sophie herself was becoming more acutely aware of the shaking and would go to her locker at every opportunity to let out what we now know to be tics, behind the locker door – an image which I find heartbreaking. In the classroom, in an effort not to be noticed, she began to seek out the back, right-hand corner. She must have felt so bewildered by what was happening to her, so out of control. The storm clouds were gathering ...

As she moved into her teens the head tics worsened and, slowly and insidiously, other unusual and repetitive movements began to appear, such as wrist-shaking, jerky eye movements and jaw stretching. The latter became so bad at one time that she would repeatedly dislocate her jaw throughout the day and the dentist made her a special brace to restrict the movement of her jaw. In typical Sophie fashion, she lost it after one day! She would also sniff a lot, much to Jack's disgust – "Mum, make her stop that noise. She's getting on my nerves" – But our family is full of allergies and I put the sniffing down to rhinitis.

At the age of nine, my father, Sophie's granddad, had watched her playing on his piano and realised that she was able to pick out tunes and copy musical phrases without difficulty. He bought her an old piano and she began to have lessons. She learned very quickly, passing her Grade 1 exam in weeks without having to look at the music. But, by her mid-teens, the tics were interfering with her playing and her music teacher would frequently tell her to keep still. This, in turn, made her tics worse, until just sitting at the piano would provoke her tics.

At school, her teachers described her as scatty, but her grades were fine. She rarely brought home any homework, although other mothers of children at the school would complain to me about the volume of work which their daughters were being given. We somehow knew, intuitively, that we must not put any undue pressure on Sophie. Outside school, she was always pushing the boundaries, and again, we strongly felt that a heavy-handed approach would be counter-productive and might alienate her. Consequently she was allowed to do things that her brother had not been allowed to do at the same age, and that were really against our better judgement.

This approach was very difficult in practice, because it constantly left us feeling as though we were failing as parents. But, with hindsight, I think our approach was right. It allowed us to stay on good terms with Sophie, and therefore be in the best position to help her.

Then the storm broke ...

... I was sitting in my classroom one morning, in the middle of teaching a maths lesson, when the school secretary burst through the door. Sophie had had an asthma attack and the ambulance had been called. I flew to my car and drove to Sophie's school with a sickening lump in my stomach and a thousand thoughts and images racing through my mind. As I turned the corner into the school road, there was the ambulance, its doors gaping open and its lights flashing.

I tore down the corridor and eventually found Sophie slumped on the floor, being attended to by the ambulancemen surrounded by her stunned classmates and ashen-faced PE teacher. Sophie was semi-conscious and I was convinced that she was going to die, right there in front of me. The paramedics gave her oxygen and then we drove to the hospital where her condition, thankfully, gradually improved. The doctors, to my surprise, then said that they were unsure whether she had actually had an asthma attack. They felt it could have been a panic attack, even though she had suffered from mild asthma since she was eleven.

This same scenario was to repeat itself several times over the next few months, and I became so anxious, that whenever my classroom door opened, my throat tightened and my stomach churned. On one occasion, Sophie was out with some friends when she suffered a very bad panic attack and was kept in hospital overnight, as she was unconscious when she arrived at the hospital, and they had suspected that she had taken an Ecstasy tablet. She had not.

No follow-up help was ever offered after these episodes. We were just left to get on with it. At this stage, we still had not connected Sophie's strange movements with the panic attacks. We just knew that there was something very, very wrong, and we felt powerless to help.

Meanwhile, Sophie was encountering difficulties with her friendships at school. From my own experience as a teacher, I know that girls can be very treacherous in their dealings with each other. Sophie and her friends were no exception. She had lots of friends, but they straddled two different groups. Sometimes this created conflict and she had to make those awkward decisions which all teenagers have to make in an effort to fit in. On one occasion, on the last day of term before the Easter holidays in her fourth year, she made the wrong decision, and was ostracised by the whole year group. One very powerful girl had managed to persuade all the others that this would be fun. For Sophie, it was catastrophic.

She came home distraught and vowed that she wouldn't set foot in the school again. We tried to argue that everything would be fine after the holidays, and it might have been, but she was adamant. We went to see the head and told her what had happened. She, in turn, tried to reassure us that everything would be alright, but at the same time told us that the same thing had happened to her own daughter in the sixth form, for no apparent reason, and, despite being the head of her daughter's school, she had been powerless to do anything about it. It had persisted until she left the school. This, coupled with Sophie's determination to leave, and the fact that the school had been less than sympathetic when she had had her panic attacks (one of the secretaries used to tell her to stop panicking!) made us decide that the only option was to move her.

The move to a new school was not to be a happy one, although Sophie still insists that it was the right one. Another selective school, this one was co-educational, and we hoped the presence of boys might prove beneficial. What we didn't expect was that in this school she would be bullied on a daily basis by two girls, Leanne and Sally. They had found out why Sophie had left her previous school and began to taunt her. They also hated the attention which Sophie immediately attracted from the boys (she was, and still is, a very pretty girl). Sophie, by this stage, already had a steady boyfriend, so she wasn't interested in any of the boys, but probably enjoyed all the attention. She and her boyfriend were together for four years and he helped her through her most difficult years, for which we will always be grateful.

Sophie bumped into Leanne, several years later, when they were both at university in Manchester. Despite hating confrontation, she approached her in Sainsbury's supermarket and asked why she had tormented her the way she did. Leanne – on her own – stammered out an apology and admitted that her behaviour had been appalling. It was a defining and empowering moment for Sophie – a laying to rest of a powerful ghost from her past.

So, what with the bullying from Leanne and her equally nasty mate, Sally, the constant anxiety of trying to hide or disguise her ticcing in this new environment, and changing courses in the middle of her GCSEs, Sophie's panic attacks continued. She received much more sympathy from the new staff, particularly the school secretary, who allowed her to go to her room if ever she felt too stressed. She also made some good friends, among them two girls who stood up for her against the bullies and a boy who is still one of her best friends today. But the school was run on very strict lines and it must have been pure purgatory for her at times.

By now, Sophie was sinking into depression, bewildered by all the terrible things that were happening to her, she must have felt that her world was falling apart. We had been to see our two family doctors on numerous occasions, and each time we would be told to ignore the tics, she would probably grow out of them. If only Sophie had been able to ignore them – if only other people had been able to ignore them. Eventually we demanded to see a psychiatrist to try and deal with the panic attacks and depression. We saw several, none of whom had the first clue as to what could be the matter. As a mother, I was prime fodder for the psychiatrists' theorising, the general conclusion being that Sophie and I were too close.

When Sophie was about fifteen, I read an article about Tourette Syndrome in *The Times* newspaper. The phrase which jumped out at me was 'tics which change over time'. For the first time I had some insight into what was going on. I remember telephoning my sister about it, because she teaches in an adolescent psychiatric unit, and saying that I was sure that Sophie did not have Tourettes, but that I suspected the problem was neurological. She agreed. I took the article to my GP and asked for Sophie to be referred to a neurologist.

In the meantime, he had arranged for an appointment with a new consultant psychiatrist after one of Sophie's panic attacks. After an hour with Sophie, this man, who shall be nameless, came into the waiting room where I was sitting.

"You have a lovely daughter," he began.

"Yes, she is, isn't she? But she's very depressed. Have you managed to find out what's wrong with her?" I asked. "Does she need to see a neurologist?"

"A neurologist? No! I've told you, she's a lovely girl. Just going through a bit of a bad patch."

"Yes, but what do you think is the problem?"

"Mmm … I'm not sure, but I think I know someone who might be able to help her."

He then proceeded to give me the name and address of a therapist. The only problem was that it would cost us £41 per hour and she lived about twenty miles away. His parting words to Sophie were, "I'll promise you this, Sophie, I won't discharge you until you're perfectly happy and you discharge yourself." She hasn't heard from him since!

Unfortunately, at that stage, my faith in the medical profession was still more or less intact, so I took his advice and cancelled Sophie's appointment with the neurologist.

The therapist turned out to be a complete waste of time and money. On her second visit Sophie came out distraught. The therapist had just sat there waiting for Sophie to speak for the best part of an hour. What therapeutic value this was supposed to have eluded us. After six months with the therapist, Sophie was still just as depressed, anxious and ticcy.

The last session Sophie spent with her was on a day when she was particularly ticcy. Her condition worsened during the session and the therapist had to put a blanket down for her on the carpet. She was very alarmed by what she witnessed, and at the end of the session she called me in from my car. She described what had happened and suggested that I make an appointment for Sophie to see a neurologist. So, after wasting six months, we went back to our GP and he referred us, yet again, to a local neurologist. At this point I should say that, although, like many doctors, our GP did not have any real knowledge about Tourettes, he was prepared to learn, and did everything in his power to help Sophie. He still always asks about her today, even though she is no longer his patient.

The tics increased relentlessly and Sophie would come to me and beg for me to help them stop. I felt completely helpless, but I told her I would not give up until I had explored every possible avenue. The spasms around her head and neck caused a great deal of pain and I took her to a masseuse at least once a week. The effects were always short-lived, but they did give her some relief. Later, she saw a reflexologist, with similar results. She also saw a hypnotherapist, but nothing seemed to work. She also began to have slight vocal tics, which were barely noticeable, but which she found very embarrassing.

Eventually, the appointment with the neurologist came and the three of us sat in the waiting room full of apprehension. We were called in and, after asking about Sophie's symptoms, she was told that, yes, she definitely did have Tourette Syndrome. To each of her questions the answers were stark – yes, she might start swearing, yes, it could get worse, yes, her children might be born with it and, yes, it was a lifelong illness. Not a lot of grounds for optimism there! The consultant's abrupt delivery of this life sentence was cold and cruel, and we were determined that Sophie should not see him again.

It was about this time, just before her sixteenth birthday, that things reached crisis point. She had taken nine GCSEs and as the summer wore on, she had convinced herself that she would fail them all, or do very badly. On the night before the results, I heard a horrible wailing coming from the bathroom. I ran upstairs to find Sophie sobbing uncontrollably, having taken several Paracetamol. It was not a serious attempt at suicide, but she was feeling suicidal. My husband and I spent the rest of that night desperately trying to convince her that the GCSEs didn't matter, *she* was all that mattered. We told her that we knew that life was very difficult for her at the moment, but it *would* get better. She just had to hang on.

She collected her results the next day – nearly all As. Her mood lifted for about an hour, then the depression took over once more, and the tics, which made her every waking moment an exhausting, painful, embarrassing nightmare, continued. Business as usual!

When it came to going back into the sixth form, we were expecting trouble. I often used to ask myself how I would cope in Sophie's situation, and I knew that I would have crumbled. She was so strong and stoical, it was very humbling watching her cope. I drove her to the school for three days and her mood got blacker and blacker. On the fourth day we picked up one of her friends on the way. She was busily chatting to Sophie from the back seat, but Sophie was not responding. I looked over at her and saw that she was struggling to hold back the tears. When we reached the school gates, I told her friend to go in, Sophie would follow in a moment. I then turned to Sophie, "You can't do this, can you, love?" She burst into tears and, after a long hug, I said, "Well, you don't have to. Let's go home and have a think about it."

The week before, I had bumped into one of the mums from Sophie's junior school. I hadn't seen her for over six years. She had told me that her daughter, and two other girls from the school had gone to a community college sixth form, about six miles away from where we lived. I knew that they were the type of parents who would have chosen carefully for their daughter, so I made enquiries. By that afternoon, Sophie had not only enrolled in the college, but was sitting in a history lesson.

She never looked back. The staff at the college could not have been kinder and more understanding and the flexibility of the timetable suited Sophie. If she didn't have a lecture she could go home. On Wednesdays she had no lectures, so it gave her a day's respite in the middle of the week. The panic attacks did not stop completely, but if she went into panic attack mode, or became very twitchy, the staff would ring me and I would collect her and take her home.

Her symptoms were really severe during the whole of the sixth form, and she missed approximately one third of the A Level course. Often her eyes would not keep still long enough for her to read her books, and I had to read many of her A Level texts out loud to her. Similarly, she was far too twitchy to type her essays and she either wrote them by hand, or dictated them to me. At this time, the tics would affect virtually every area of her body, and she became very worried about the long-term damage she might be doing to her joints.

One of her A Level subjects was theatre studies and for the group practical the class decided to do a play about Tourettes, which they wrote and was put on in the local theatre, with Sophie in the starring role. Whilst on stage she barely twitched, despite being very twitchy all day and everyday. At this stage her confidence was still very high. Unfortunately, over the years she has lost confidence – not surprising when suffering from such an obvious and embarrassing affliction – but her self-esteem is still very much intact. In fact, she is proud that she has survived such a devastating illness, and in many ways, has achieved far more than her healthy peers.

A simple solution to her lack of organisational skills whilst at college, was the use of plastic pockets for her work. Any work that she did, or pieces of paper that she was given, were immediately put into these pockets, and she took great pride in her beautifully neat files. She also enjoyed being in a mixed ability group where she could shine.

Just before she took her A Levels, both my parents died within hours of each other – my mum after a long illness, and my dad, very suddenly. Most of the family, including Sophie, was with them when they died. She showed the most amazing maturity, throughout this most difficult of times, and I was very proud of both her and Jack. I did worry what effect such a hugely stressful event would have on her illness, but, in the event, she coped remarkably well. She was very, very sad, and still misses them very much, but she did not go to pieces. This, to me, proved that she is a survivor and has great strength of character. Two months later she had to sit her A Levels, which she passed with three excellent grades and won a place at Manchester University to study Drama and Screen Studies.

She was still studying the piano but was getting so twitchy around it that she was forced to abandon it in the middle of learning her Grade 8 pieces. To me, it was doubly sad, because I had read of other Tourettes sufferers whose tics disappeared completely when they were playing. Even Mozart was thought to have Tourettes. She has just begun to play again, aged twenty-two, and it is music to my ears!

After she had seen the first neurologist, I got in touch with the Tourettes Association. Through their helpline I learned that Sophie probably had all sorts of other issues going on inside her head that I might not know about. Indeed there were. She told me about horrific mental images that tortured her all the time, I already knew that she often suffered nightmares and disturbed sleep patterns. We also came to realise that she suffered from OCD and had many secret rituals around lamp-posts, clothes, hot things, etc. She also had the compulsion to even things up. If I kissed her on one cheek, I then had to kiss her on the other. If this procedure did not produce the 'just right' feeling, then the kissing would have to start again. In the same way, if she accidentally burnt a finger on anything, she would then have the urge to burn the other in exactly the same way. She also had strong urges to touch hot things.

We also learned that Dr Hugh Rickards was our nearest specialist, despite his clinic being ninety miles away. After much pushing by our GP, we secured an appointment, just after Christmas, in that first term in sixth form college. It was a great relief to talk to someone who knew everything there was to know (except how to cure it!) about the disease, and his caring, sympathetic attitude was in sharp contrast to the first neurologist. Dr Rickards tried to paint an optimistic picture, and said that the usual pattern was for the illness to peak in the teens, or early twenties, and then subside. He felt that by the time Sophie was in her late twenties, she would be left with nothing more than a few facial tics.

He soon established Sophie on a drug regime of Sulpiride for her tics and

Seroxat for her depression and OCD. From the start, the side effects of the drugs made normal life almost impossible. It was fortunate that she was no longer at a nine-to-five school, because, left alone, she would sleep through to late afternoon. When she was awake, she felt so lethargic that she could barely drag herself around. The Sulpiride did lessen the tics for a while, but they were still interfering with her everyday life, and the Seroxat did reduce the OCD and the depression, but at the expense of dulling her perception. She just did not feel she was herself, and she didn't like it. She tried Haloperidol for a while, but the side effects were just as severe. The side effect which she found the most distressing, was excessive weight gain. She lost her beautiful slender figure, putting on over two stone in just over a year. She was also frightened of the possibility of very serious, long-term side effects.

By the end of sixth form she was absolutely drained and exhausted; from the drugs, the stress of the exams and the illness itself, which was taking a huge toll. She decided to take a year out, during which she would try, with Dr Rickards' guidance, to establish a medication regime that would work for her. She was offered a job in the marketing department of the college and gladly accepted. The job was wonderful, involving all kinds of opportunities and responsibilities and she also did quite a lot of modelling for the college's marketing material. Unfortunately, she also fell asleep in meetings, struggled to get up in the mornings, due to her medication, and became very anxious trying to conceal her tics when in public for long periods of time. She discussed it with us and we suggested going part-time, but the college felt that she needed to take time off to get herself well for university. So, very reluctantly, she had to give up the job.

For the rest of that year, she struggled along. Life was going on around her, as her youth passed her by. Jack and Sophie's college friends had long since gone to university, while she was still stuck at home. I left teaching and could therefore devote all my attention to Sophie. If she had been particularly bad the day before, the temptation was to let her sleep on the following day, often until mid-afternoon. I would watch her sleeping – my beautiful, talented, lovely daughter – so serene and peaceful. I would hesitate to wake her, knowing that to do so would put her once again in the clutches of this horrible thing that had taken over her young life.

During her gap year, she and her boyfriend of four years split up. It was her choice, but he had stood by her through some very difficult times and she still had great affection for him and hated hurting him. The ups and downs of adolescence are difficult for everyone, but for anyone suffering from TS, the downs are so much worse, because stress exacerbates the condition. Any emotional upset, no matter how small, would result in a rapid worsening of her condition. I soon learnt to hold my tongue, no matter how trying things became, because any criticism, particularly from me, would unleash a torrent of twitching.

On one terrible occasion Sophie had been glass painting in the sitting room. She is very artistic and would spend hours painting intricate designs on glassware and then sell them at the college. She found that painting made her tics virtually disappear, so it was very therapeutic. What she was not so good at was preparation, and on this day she had been painting without putting newspaper down on my brand new carpet. Of course, the inevitable happened and a whole jar of red paint spilt over an enormous patch of blue carpet, right in the middle of the room. I just exploded with anger, and screamed at Sophie, a part of me knowing what my rage would do to her, but I couldn't stop myself. Within seconds, her body was convulsing from head to toe, and I was hugging her, apologising over and over again.

The guilt I felt was awful, but the rational part of me told me that I'm only human. The stress of watching your child's life fall apart, whilst at the same time trying to sound optimistic all the time and hide your own emotions, builds up inside you like a pressure cooker. Just occasionally, when your guard is down, the pressure forces an escape.

At about this time, Sophie applied for, and was eventually awarded, Disability Living Allowance, at the higher level for mobility, because her illness prevented her from using public transport on her own. If she was sitting next to someone on a bus, she would keep turning her head towards them, which did not go down very well. She also has difficulty walking at times; she has strange knee bends, frozen postures and sometimes her eyes refuse to look straight ahead, so she can't see where she is going. This happened once when she was with us in Paris, and we had to lead her like a blind person. She received the lower level for care, because she can do most things for herself, except when her symptoms are severe, although she needs a very high level of emotional support, even now. The allowance is paid regardless of whether you are in or out of work. She is still receiving the benefit now, aged twenty-two, but she has had to fight to get it, due to the level of ignorance about the illness amongst professionals.

As the start of the university term loomed ever nearer, Sophie grew more and more apprehensive. She had insisted on living away from home, as she felt that her home city held too many painful memories for her. She desperately wanted a new start, and part of her probably hoped that by leaving home, she might also leave behind her illness.

The university's special needs department couldn't have been kinder, or more helpful. Anything and everything that Sophie needed was put in place, from note-takers to computers which responded to human speech. But none of it was to prove to be enough. She survived for a year and a half, passing all her exams, and in many ways having a great time, but sitting in a lecture theatre was well nigh impossible for her and the pressure of trying to complete assignments when she couldn't even sit still, never mind think straight, was just too much. A lot of friends who she had made, like many before them, lost interest when she was too ill to socialise, or was too ticcy to go out, and she started to become very depressed in the first term of her second year.

Many good things came out of Sophie's year and a half at university. She gained her independence and has lived away from home ever since. She loved the practical side of the course and learnt a lot about film and has gone on to become an independent film-maker. She had a lot of fun, and most importantly, she met her husband-to-be, Matt. It was good old-fashioned love at first sight, and they have now been together for three and a half years and are getting married this September (2003). Since they met, he has seen Sophie in the depths of despair, tortured by tics and struggling to come to terms with TS, but also, most of the time, happy, funny and full of life. His acceptance of her condition is total. In their first summer together they spent seven weeks travelling in Thailand, bringing back many wonderful memories. We were naturally nervous about her going, because of her illness, but delighted that she had achieved such a level of independence. In the event, she was fine, her symptoms virtually disappearing as she relaxed in the heat with Matt.

When they got back from Thailand, Sophie announced that she was sick of being on medication and was determined to get off it. The first drug to go was Seroxat, which recently has had a very bad press – some people who have wanted to withdraw from the drug have become even more depressed and even suicidal. This certainly happened in Sophie's case – by Christmas she was back in the throes of deep depression. This could have been brought on by her realisation that she might not be able to complete her university course, a worry that she had not really shared with anyone, although I knew that she was unhappy.

Ever since she went away, we had been in daily contact with her by mobile phone. We would sometimes talk three or four times a day. It was a lifeline when she wasn't feeling good (we still speak on the phone virtually every day, and see her about once week). If things got really bad, I would drop everything and drive to Manchester to see her, and still do. I can usually find something to cheer her up.

Then, one day, just before Christmas 1999, she didn't answer her phone. I rang throughout the day, leaving messages – still nothing. I rang Matt. Had he seen her? No. He ran to her friend's house – she wasn't there. I felt as if a huge, yawning void, stretching way into the future, had opened up. Where was she? Was she alright? Please let nothing have happened to her …

Then, finally, she answered the phone. She was in her car, she wasn't sure where, somewhere on the outskirts of Manchester. No, she didn't want to see us, or Matt, she was too tired, she needed time by herself. I pleaded with her to come home, or to Matt's. No … she was sorry … but she just needed to be on her own … To think … To stop …

Eventually, Jack managed to get her to agree to meet Matt and they spent the night in a hotel. She came home the next morning looking totally defeated. But at least we had her back. Whatever her problems were, we could sort them out, as we had always done before. It all came pouring out. She didn't see how she could continue with her course. We reminded her that she didn't have to stay if she didn't want to. No one had written the script for her life – she could do what she wanted. She was visibly relieved, and has never regretted her decision to leave. The university assured her that she could resume the course whenever she wanted, but at the moment, she has no intentions of taking up the offer.

Since that point, she and Matt have been living together and her life has steadily improved. She is working as a freelance film-maker and photographer with equipment which we have provided. Having enough money to provide her with such things, as well as on-going financial support, has allowed her to do things in her own time, and is a significant factor in her improvement. It has removed the urgency and pressure of having to earn her own living. She will get there in the end, but it will be at her own pace. I am absolutely convinced that if she had been forced to support herself too soon, she would not be as well as she is now.

The TS is still there but her symptoms are less severe. The waxing and waning still happens, but the peaks and troughs are less steep. She is receiving cognitive behavioural therapy, at her own request, and this is helping her to understand and, hopefully, change, some of her obsessive behaviours. One of the treatments which has helped her the most has been hypnotherapy. She received it on the NHS after she was diagnosed with yet another syndrome; Irritable Bowel (IBS). Her consultant was very sympathetic about her Tourettes and said that the IBS was probably related. He arranged fifteen hypnotherapy sessions, during which the therapist provided her with coping skills for many different aspects of both illnesses, from tics, to insomnia, to stomach pain, and gave her a tape to use at home. She found the sessions very helpful and still uses the tape and the techniques she learnt.

During her teenage years, Sophie used to smoke cannabis, with our approval. It gave immediate relief of her symptoms and it was the one drug which helped her through her teenage years. She also smoked tobacco for a time, as this gave relief to a lesser extent and could be used in situations where cannabis was not acceptable. Of course, cannabis is illegal at the moment and also very expensive. Sophie always knew that she would have to give up the drug eventually because she wants to have children. Also, she is very health-conscious and hates smoking.

So, on her twenty-first birthday, she gave up tobacco, except in a cannabis joint, and this year, on New Year's Day, she gave up smoking cannabis and has not smoked anything for five months. She did this because she had managed to persuade her consultant to include her in a pilot study on the use of cannabis in Tourettes. She was given a supply of the drug, in tablet form, and takes one when her symptoms are bad. Most weeks she does not take anything at all, but it is comforting for her to have them there as a safety net, or if she knows she is going to be in a particularly stressful situation. Much more research needs to be done into the properties of this powerful drug, which obviously has considerable medicinal potential for a range of conditions.

Sophie is now looking to the future with real hope. She and Matt both want children and have accepted that they could have a child with Tourettes. Dr Rickards has advised Sophie that she stands about a one in nineteen chance of having a child as badly affected as herself, and she and Matt feel strong enough to face that risk together. Any child they have will be loved just as much as we love Sophie and Jack.

Since Sophie's diagnosis, we realise that my father also had TS, although not as severely as Sophie. He was a wonderful, funny person who loved life and we all loved him. I am one of seven children, and we are all unaffected. My father was also one of seven, and he was the only one with TS, although one of his sisters did have slight facial tics. My husband also has very slight facial tics, but no other Tourette-like symptoms and no other members of his family are affected. Clearly there are lots of factors at work here, as well as the genetic ones. Hopefully, research will uncover the mysteries which lie behind the illness, and eventually find a cure, or at least, more effective treatments with less side effects.

Sophie is not our daughter's real name – she wishes to remain anonymous, not because she is ashamed of her illness, or has not come to terms with it, but because she does not want to be defined by it. In no way does she see herself as a 'Touretter' – a term which she feels is demeaning – she is a *person*, who, unfortunately, also has Tourettes. Although this may look as if she is burying her head in the sand, I feel that it is a healthy attitude and is her way of coping. She is more than happy for me to tell her story, as it may be of help to other sufferers.

Of course, it has been devastating to discover that we have unwittingly passed on this terrible, baffling illness to our beautiful daughter, but we are determined to continue doing all we can to lessen its impact. At the moment I think we are winning the battle – the future looks bright – the clouds are finally lifting.

SURVIVING WITH HOPE

Jenny Worth's Story by her Mum, Sue

Is it a dream? No, it's a memory I thought I would never see again. Jenny – my lovely thirteen-year-old daughter – washed, dressed and going to school HAPPY, even if it is only two hours in the afternoon at the moment. Perhaps you're thinking that's perfectly normal behaviour, but to me it was like heaven, so why am I crying my heart out?

It all began with a phone call to say, sorry, the school won't take your daughter. The months of waiting in hope to hear from a school which we thought was the very best for our daughter – a decision with which the LEA and the Child and Adolescent Mental Health Service (CAMHS) had agreed – had finally come to an end. But the sudden reason for the school's decision to remove her was that there was a boy there who was upsetting our daughter too much, and they thought she would benefit more by being in a residential situation. Unfortunately the residential school only took boys.

Looking back, should I have been more forceful and insistent? I'm only a parent whose gut feeling says there's something wrong. I had a long talk with the special needs teachers about my daughter's comments to me; how many eight-year-olds say they want to die? I had interviews with headteachers and doctors, during which my daughter shows no signs of facial grimaces or noises. Was I imagining them? Outside again and all the symptoms would reappear. Professionals obviously have specialist knowledge, yet they saw nothing at the beginning. The facial grimaces, the blinking and the noises were dismissed as, "only nervous tics", or they would be attributed to problems with another child's behaviour in the classroom ; "All the other children cope with this boy, so your daughter can." In the end, because she was unable to cope, and became very frustrated, she hit out and landed a punch on the bully's nose. So now she's the problem child.

It took us a year on the waiting list to get an appointment with CAMHS, and after attending for six months, this, too, was threatening to come to an end because her caseworker was retiring. However, our comments on this news must have got through to someone, and we received a hospital appointment within a week, where she was diagnosed with Tourette Syndrome. Amazingly, though, I was the one who first broached the subject of TS, but, unfortunately, the only consultant who really knew anything about the disease had died and it was to be another year before steady appointments with a permanent psychiatrist were arranged. In the meantime, we were able to see other consultants from outside the area, but because there would be no continuity, it wasn't possible to alter medication, and appointments at other hospitals didn't materialise. One hospital actually gave us an appointment, but then cancelled it when they found out CAMHS were getting more staff.

The sheer frustration of life over the passage of time was taking its toll. Our daughter had been out of full-time education for almost two years. If she had learning difficulties and was unable to keep up with most of the work set for her age, or if she was a rebellious, disruptive child, I'm sure she would still be in school. But she has TS and OCD, very low self-esteem (in my view only to be expected with the way her life has been), school phobia (which doesn't really exist according to some professionals), and panic attacks. The response of the system has been to say, let's hurt her some more and deny her access to the full curriculum and socialisation found in schools, even though it is not her fault that there are no local schools with specialist help. Don't get me wrong, I do realise that other people have problems and need help, but so does she. My hope now is that we *will* find a school suitable for Jenny, and we are determined that she will *not* be denied an education, or any opportunity for self-fulfilment and employment.

It now seems as if there is light at the end of the tunnel, after all. Two schools have been mentioned. One is a weekly boarding school, which, after much soul-searching, we are coming round to agreeing to. After all, Jenny is my daughter, whom I love, but after so much straining to survive on her part, and all of us coping through so many ups and downs, I am beginning to question whether I have handled things badly. Am I a good mother? Perhaps it has to be a case of being cruel to be kind. Jenny could have the opportunity here of a good education, the chance to forge new friendships, and have a better social life with people who understand her condition and will give her stability.

The other school is also residential, but on a termly basis, which, in effect would mean me losing my daughter. But it does take people who have TS. However, I looked twice at this brochure to make sure I was not dreaming, for, despite recognising that people with this condition need specialised help, its fees are £2,000 per week. Yes! That is £80,000 for a forty-week year! Somehow I cannot see the LEA providing this amount, so how many special needs children are being denied an education because families face the problems of funding?

As time has gone on, school availability and our thoughts on which school to choose have changed. We have come to the conclusion that our daughter does need residential care. But the final result seems to be that one of the schools can't meet her needs, although no detailed explanation has been given, and the other has no places available. We did visit another school, but found the atmosphere and facilities unacceptable. However, even if any of these schools were suitable and could take Jenny, there are simply not enough funds available.

Time to get our local MP involved, yet again. Another meeting with the LEA to sort out where we go from here, and what schools and funding are available. More school lists are looked at. We spend hours looking on the Internet, reading Ofsted reports. There are plenty of schools if Jenny was a boy and had more severe learning difficulties! The official schools database, of over 31,000 schools, is categorised according to special needs and disabilities, but not for children with TS. So Jenny's notes are sent to more schools and more visits are arranged. One of them has plenty of staff, and a caring environment, but fortunately or unfortunately, Jenny is too intelligent and wouldn't be able to cope with coming to terms with her condition and being in an environment with others with more severe conditions. We are waiting to hear if one of the other schools has any places.

"Bitch, whore, shut up. F... off, stupid." Can these words be coming out of my daughter's mouth? Yes, but they are her cries for attention, the only way for her to express her anger and frustration. She knows my opinion about swearing and how she speaks to me. She knows it is not acceptable. Then, out of her next breath, "STAY ..." as I leave the room. Not long afterwards she is telling me how much she loves me and I'm the best mum in the world. I feel so helpless, not being able to make her feel good about herself and her life. It is heartbreaking to see her scraping her face and screaming, "Get it out", begging for help. She just doesn't know what to do. There are voices in her head, or she is having day-mares. She wants to die and asks me to kill her, then things will be better. She even works out ways of dying. In contrast, she is forever apologising, even after you have told her she has done nothing wrong. Then she is cursing or hitting out at me.

Our worry, when she has run out of the house, clinic, or school, is unbearable, but so far, she has always come back and the police have been involved only once. She has even sat on the pavement near our house in her nightclothes, refusing to come back in. If I try to speak to her, she only gets more agitated.

Finally, a school has said YES! They would love to have Jenny, from 9 September. They were impressed by her. Now for the problem of funding. The LEA is going back to the county moderation panel for more funds, as we have only been allocated enough for a day school. We need approximately another £20,000. Our first attempt at getting more funds failed. This route was the quickest way. The other route is to obtain funds from the Health Authority and this will again take time. Our MP is backing

170

us and wants to hear the result immediately.

SUCCESS!!! The relief. Time for the bottle of champagne we have been saving. One more hurdle overcome, but we will survive, with hope, through other situations, of which I'm sure there will be many more. My message to anyone reading this is – DON'T give up hope.

MY LIFE STORY

Jenny Worth, aged thirteen

From the age of seven I knew I was different from the rest of the crowd. At the time, I didn't realise what I was doing, or what these strange urges were. Even if I was ticcing all the time, I didn't realise why I was teased so badly. Then my Mum started to tell me to, "Stop doing that", and all I could say was, "What do you mean, Mum? I'm not doing anything." Then she told me about the screeching noises and the nodding I was so often doing. Then I started realising what I was actually doing and why people were teasing me.

Looking back, I remember my Mum saying as I was walking to school, "If you stop doing that, I'll treat you to something special", or, "if you don't stop doing that, I'm going to get a neck brace for you". Now I realise she meant no harm, all she was trying to do was help me. I am finding it hard to type this bit as I can't always express my feelings of anger and depression in very much detail, but all I know is that no one should be left on their own feeling like they can't go out because someone might happen to call them names.

I don't really know why I sometimes feel as if I shouldn't be living, or why I'm saying sorry to my mum or my dad every five seconds, even if I haven't done or said anything wrong, and then stupid me says sorry for saying sorry, then saying sorry for saying sorry again, and as you can see, I could carry on saying sorry over and over and over again.

I moved from one school to another until I got diagnosed at the age of ten. I am thirteen now and still struggling with my obsessions, especially the school obsession. I now find it really hard to go to school any more, but on good days I usually do. I have moved from a school in Leyland because I could not cope there because of the busyness and the noise going on around me.

I am now at a special needs school which is designed for children with problems with school, such as broken legs and pregnancy. I don't really like it here, as it is only for two hours a day, which is only twelve hours a week. You can hardly call that a life, can you? The other annoying thing is that I find I cannot work there because no one else is doing the same work as me, so I am trying to work, but all I can hear is teachers trying to tell the others what to do. Even though I don't like any school, my other school seems better because you get to meet others and integrate with others.

At the moment we are going through the statementing process and trying to find a suitable school. This is proving impossibly difficult. Several schools have refused me, as they don't think they can help me enough. Then there is the problem of funding my education. I am very peeved off by this!!

At times, life is hell for me. In fact, it seems to be most of the time. I feel so alone and like I am trapped in a metal box with no breathing space, or air holes. At times things get so bad that I resort to running away, but I stay within a safe distance of my home, school, or therapy sessions. I think one of the main people who has helped me is Katie Keppie and her team at CAMHS. They listen to all my problems and worries, which I find really helpful. Even though they may not be able to find all the answers, they always give me reassurance. Also, when things get bad, I may resort to scraping my face and screaming, "Get it out. Get it out. No, no, no." When I do this I simply mean, please make the Tourettes leave me alone and stop causing all this anger and pain.

I have not been able to go to school recently, because I have refused, for the simple reason that there is no point in going because they know they have let me down and not let me go anywhere decent. So, if they won't let me go anywhere decent, I shouldn't have to. After all, I don't want a rubbish school where I don't feel happy. I might as well go for the crème de la crème (best of the best).

Finally, we've found a school, but the only problem is that it's a termly boarding school, which means I don't come home until the second weekend and the holidays. The school said YES but now the problem is the funding. We still need another whopping £20,000.

HURRRRAAAY, we've got the funding, and I am starting this September.

I have found poetry helps me. Recently I entered a poem into a competition at a Disability Awareness Day held at Warrington, and it won the competition. It is called 'Disorder' and here it is …

DISORDER

Don't get stressed,
It's not worth it. Just
Sing your favourite song,
Or you will just feel wrong.
Ring a friend to talk to,
Depression is a horrid thing to do
Everyone shout Gouranga
Ready, Steady, BE HAPPY.

FACT SHEET

- Tourette Syndrome affects up to 1 in 100 schoolchildren in Britain.

- It usually begins between the ages of seven and eleven (although some cases have reported symptoms earlier), causing patients to develop repetitive twitching movements in the arms, shoulders, face, legs and trunk.

- These embarrassing movements, known as tics, are often made worse by stress and anxiety. Many people with Tourette Syndrome have a mild condition that does not require treatment, while other cases are so severe that medication is needed.

- In addition to the involuntary movements, patients make involuntary noises, for example grunting, groans, yelps and howls, or complete words or sentences. Sufferers may repeat what other people have said, or copy their gestures. A small minority of the more severe cases suffer from Coprolalia (involuntary swearing).

- People with Tourette Syndrome commonly suffer from other associated disorders, including obsessional behaviours and hyperactivity/attention deficit.

- The condition is three to four times more common in boys than girls and is usually inherited, although there is no genetic test for Tourette Syndrome and it is not yet possible to predict the likelihood of a child being affected.

- Children and adults with Tourette Syndrome deserve to be assessed and treated by specialists with experience of the condition. The correct diagnosis and management are vital to allow optimal schooling and work performance.

- The condition tends to fluctuate in severity and often improves after adolescence. There is no medical cure, but a variety of medications can be used to help the condition, including those that affect a chemical in the brain known as dopamine. Such medication (in larger doses) is also used to treat Schizophrenia, although there is no connection between the two disorders.

Dr Jeremy Stern
Chairman of Tourette Syndrome (UK) Association.

If you are not already a member of the Tourette Syndrome (UK) Association, please consider joining. The work of the Association is funded entirely by membership subscriptions and donations, and the strength of our voice lies in our numbers. Donations are always most gratefully received.

Tourette Syndrome (UK) Association is a registered charity dedicated to providing support for sufferers and their families, as well as educating, informing, campaigning and promoting medical research on behalf of all those affected by TS.

PO box 26149
Dunfermline KY12 7YU

Helpline 0845 458 1252
Admin 01383 629600
Email enquiries@tsa.org.uk
Website www.tsa.org.uk